C000111672

dowe.
desire

Brownell

REUSE
REPAIR
RECYCLE

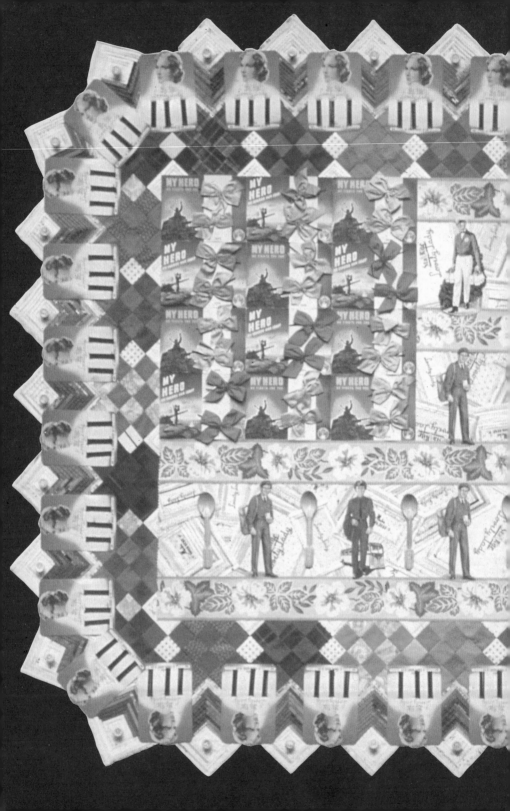

REUSE REPAIR RECYCLE

A MINE OF CREATIVE IDEAS FOR THRIFTY LIVING

Jan McHarry

Gaia Books Limited

A Gaia Original

Project editor	Jo Godfrey Wood
Project designer	Sara Mathews
Direction	Joss Pearson
	Patrick Nugent

This is a Registered Trade Mark of Gaia Books Limited

First published in the United Kingdom in 1993 by
Gaia Books Limited
66 Charlotte Street   and   20 High Street
London W1P 1LR   Stroud, Glos. GL5 1AS

Copyright © 1993 Gaia Books Limited
Text copyright © 1993 Jan McHarry

All rights reserved including the right of reproduction in whole or in
part in any form

The right of Jan McHarry to be identified as the author of this work
has been asserted in accordance with Sections 77 and 78 of the
Copyright, Designs and Patents Act 1988, United Kingdom
A catalogue record for this book is available from the British Library
Printed in Denmark by Nørhaven A/S

ISBN 1 85675 045 0

10 9 8 7 6 5 4 3 2 1

Dedication

To my mother Hazel and to
the memory of my late
father, who both made so
much possible. And to
Lauren - may her generation
be more resourceful.

"Handkerchief Farewell" (previous page)
Ilisha Helfman's "quilt", 1991, is made from folded and layered papers, pleated and stitched fabrics, computerized embroidery, hand-pieced quilt squares, disposable spoons, china drawer handles, buttons, and wallpaper borders.

HOW TO USE THIS BOOK

Part 1 of the book, Ideas and Action, provides information on the processes, practices, and guiding principles in waste reduction and recycling. This sets the context for later material and establishes the complex issues and questions that surround the recovery and reuse of waste. Part 2, The World of Recycling, provides a snapshot of what is being done in selected countries throughout the world. Examples of successes and failures elsewhere can trigger others to set up new ventures and seeing how other people's visions become translated into reality can provide salutary lessons. Part 3, The Recycler's A to Z gives myriad suggestions for reusing and recycling materials, as well as providing facts and figures on recycling today. Words printed in bold throughout refer you on to an entry in the section. Use the Resources list as a signpost to further information and practical help.

Please note that the views represented in this book are the author's own and should not be taken to represent the policies of the National Recycling Forum.

CONTENTS

Toys (previous page) made by street children in Nairobi, Kenya.

The Recycler's A to Z 97

FOREWORD

It has always seemed to me that if we cannot get it right on recycling, then our prospects for learning to live sustainably on Planet Earth are just about zero.

It is not that recycling is necessarily all that easy to get right - as this book makes abundantly clear - but rather because it is one thing that we can all contribute to with relatively little inconvenience and no additional cost.

Unbelievably, however, we are still not getting it right. After years of tireless campaigning by environmentalists; after the belated but welcome recognition by industry that it too has a major role to play; after the equally welcome commitment by central government that 25 per cent of the UK's domestic waste should be recycled by the end of the decade; after umpteen opinion polls and surveys demonstrating consistently enthusiastic support from the general public for one recycling initiative or another; after all that, we are still not getting it right. Not by a very long chalk.

And the truth is that despite all that enthusiasm and support, attitudes to recycling are often extremely superficial. It is rarely seen as just one element in a much broader waste management strategy. Indeed, it is often treated as little more than a tokenistic sop to allay nagging doubts that somehow we ought to be doing more about the environment.

Take bottle banks for instance. There is something very rewarding about recycling bottles. Those nagging doubts ease even as one waits for the reassuring noise of the bottles crashing down into the bottle bank. It is the ecological equivalent of going to confession; bearing all your past sins in your arms, offering them up, receiving absolution in the shattering of the glass, secure in the knowledge that it will be melted down and made into new bottles.

"Tin can knights" (previous page), by Malcolm Fowler, is made from recycled food cans, feathers, can openers, and moulding material. The artist was inspired by the sight of motor cyclists encased and unrecognizable in their protective clothing, and wanted to point out a connection between old and new styles of self-protection.

The drinks manufacturers were well aware of this "feel good" factor when they first advocated the use of bottle banks in the early seventies. They were then under great pressure to justify their policies, and in May 1971, Friends of Earth (UK) stacked thousands of soft drinks bottles on the doorstep of Schweppes in protest at the terrible wastage in the soft drinks industry as it moved over to the use of non-returnable bottles.

But Friends of the Earth was not campaigning for the recycling of bottles. It was campaigning for the re-use of bottles. In terms of energy use and raw materials there is a big difference. Recycling is certainly better than the "one-trip" container (use it and chuck it), but nothing like as good as making use of the same bottle time after time. So why aren't the vast majority of our drinks containers reusable? It's not that people aren't enthusiastic about returnables.

Even when there is declared commitment to recycling, you get the feeling that the powers that be are just saying it because they know that's what they should be saying. For quite some time now officials have been using the language of the waste management experts, brazenly declaiming their four Rs (Reduce, Reuse, Repair, Recycle), and extolling the benefits of waste minimization.

But in truth, within many countries' government departments, recycling is still considered in isolation, a stand-alone, quick-fix that can largely be handed over to local authorities to deliver without any coherent support from central government.

As it happens, those local authorities are indeed starting to deliver in terms of implementing recycling plans. But every recycling officer you talk to will rattle off a long list of the unnecessary impediments they have to overcome and the additional costs their authorities have to bear in order to deliver.

And that's just at the local level. At the macro level governments persist with a variety of tax measures that still favour the use of virgin products, refuses to contemplate variations in tax levels to promote the use of recycled products, and remain utterly paralysed in terms of providing incentives to help develop markets for secondary materials. All the obvious policies continue to go begging. It is enough to make you recycle a few bodily fluids.

In the meantime, people are losing heart. They are keen to do their bit, many of them already are doing their bit, but they are beginning to question whether it makes any difference at all given the reluctance of government to leglislate for quicker action and the apparent intransigence of the supermarkets and industry when it comes to doing any more.

So it is highly encouraging to see such an authoritative and wide-ranging treatment of the subject as this one arriving on the scene at such a timely moment. Jan McHarry is very careful to point out, recycling is not the answer to all our waste management problems (particularly when you take into account industrial, agricultural, construction, and sewage wastes), nor is it all that we need to do as individuals.

But it is still a very important part of any lifestyle, and I hope there will be many people who will either be stirred into action or encouraged to do more by this excellent book.

Jonathon Porritt

May 1993

Linen basket (right), by Lois Walpole, is made from recycled plastic. The basic basket was made from sheet plastic acquired from a plastics factory, while the petal shapes around the rim were cut from old fabric conditioner bottles. The woven strips down the sides were made from packaging tapes.

INTRODUCTION

As I write, behind-the-scenes activity in government circles is about to give a kick-start to recycling in the UK. A major driving force is the need to sort out the economics. This is critical if recycling is to expand into a long-term option and a truly sustainable activity. Seeking common ground within the waste management industry, business and commerce, and the voluntary sector is imperative. We need to generate action rather than rhetoric and to build support through commonsense solutions based on the guiding themes of the "Polluter Pays" and the "Precautionary Principle".

There is an agreed hierarchy to waste management based on waste avoidance, reuse, materials recycling, energy recovery, and employment of the best environmental option for disposing of the remaining waste. All this sounds depressingly familiar to those who have long been advocating these practices. But now things are stirring, and in some places moving rapidly forward. Reuse and recycling are becoming key issues in corporate strategies and environmental plans. And belatedly more attention is being given to waste minimization: by no means a new subject but one that must be part of the bedrock for creating a more sustainable society. Recycling practices are, at last, gathering momentum and more and more households and workplaces can now recycle a wider variety of materials.

Writing this book has not been easy; just how far do you go in promoting pilot schemes? What happens if they don't succeed? So much varies from area to area, and from country to country that one has to be aware of making judgements based on insufficient information; a major stumbling block in assessing the true economics and full costs of recycling.

As more people become willing to sort waste there must be tangible benefits for doing this and a collection system that facilitates ease of recycling. The challenge is also placed on designers, architects, and planners to design systems - everything from kitchen units to street collection bins.

Although this book places an emphasis on what can be done at household/workplace level it does not mean that the larger waste streams are discounted. One aim is to provide enough information to get people to rethink their own practices.

Providing information that stimulates this process is the key to empowerment and action. Pressuring for change and lobbying for alternative disposal policies for other waste streams, including sewage, can then be a logical progression.

A thread running through this book is the idea that recycling is not just about collecting materials but developing and fostering initiatives that re-utilize these secondary materials. Until this happens we are not truly "closing the recycling loop". For this to happen effectively we need to look afresh at this thing called "waste". While it can be hard to break the "out of sight, out of mind" mentality, advocates of recycling are sometimes accused of sending out mixed messages that lead to frustration recycling is not just about collecting things or saving trees. This is particularly rife when gluts cause prices to drop so low that the viability of collection schemes are threatened. The recycler may then find that there is nowhere to drop off certain materials. Disillusion sets in and recycling itself is questioned.

Future planning must consider other issues, too. Access to local facilities is vital for community participation, especially where kerbside collection does not exist. And no matter how much we reduce, return, and reuse we will always need facilities such as bottle banks, can banks, and workplace schemes. Without these recycling will not flourish into a mainstream activity. However, keeping a perspective is important. Using a car just to take items for recycling may use up more energy than may be saved by recycling them. But if you cannot recycle as much as you would like you can still play a role in altering the situation. Letters do count and collective action can reverse decisions.

Bridging the gulf between what we would like to do and what we can do is a major challenge. Creating a recycling culture will not happen overnight, but to quote the late Dr Schumacher, "We must do what we conceive to be the right thing and not bother our heads or burden our souls with whether we're going to be successful".

Jan McHarry
May 1993

IDEAS
and
ACTION

"At first I thought I was fighting to save rubber trees. Then I thought I was fighting to save the Amazon rain forest. Now I realise I am fighting for humanity."
Chico Mendes

As the developed nations of the world continue to consume resources at an ever-escalating rate, we have reached the time when large corporations, industry, decision-makers, and all of us, as consumers, must begin to reconsider the long-term implications of our actions – for both the sake of humanity and the planet.

This section introduces some of the practices, processes, and collection systems that are needed to promote resource reuse and recycling. Also included are specific issues that require attention if we are serious about fostering a new approach to dealing responsibly with waste through techniques such as waste reduction, secure **landfills**, and safer **incineration**.

Globally, there is great wealth in waste. It is a "resource" with elements that can be "mined", harvested, re-utilized, re-manufactured, and recovered. But here in the industrialized nations we have lost our sense of what is valuable. Everyday items – **paper**, **plastics**, **glass**, **fabrics and textiles**, and metals – are consumed in limitless amounts. At the end of their "useful" life they are discarded as waste, as something unwanted and worthless. Without the established collection systems for recycling or energy recovery the value of waste is lost and yet more energy and resources are consumed to meet the demand for new products or raw materials. The negative impact this creates on the global ecosystem is increasingly clear.

Reuse, reclamation, and recycling are not absolute solutions to dwindling resurces, but they can buy time and reduce the need for mining, felling, or extraction.

Source reduction, waste reduction, waste minimization are all terms used to describe a priority issue – the need for everyone to become more conscious about the waste we generate and then alter some of our practices to reduce the number of disposable products we use and the overall amount of waste we create. Without waste reduction everything else can only ever be a second-best (but still necessary) option. Waste reduction must extend to cover all the waste streams – **packaging** waste is a high-profile issue, but domestic waste is only part of the problem. Keeping a perspective involves seeking solutions for dealing with the larger quantities of agricultural waste, construction and demolition materials, mining and quarrying spoil, construction debris, and sewage.

Getting the strategies right is vital for a more sustainable future, yet we are not creating something totally new. Reuse and recycling are centuries-old practices. Throughout the world salvaging other people's discards for remanufacture, repair, and renovation is by tradition widespread. In some cultures, and especially in developing countries, this is practised to such an extent that nothing is discarded and wasted at all. And for some, salvage will always be a crucial means of survival.

There is now an urgent need for the industrialized nations to rethink many of their attitudes and practices toward waste. And in taking the recycling message out into the community, we must be conscious about the definitions and terminology we use. Should we not be emphasizing that rubbish is really a waste-derived resource instead of just "waste"?

Recreating a recycling culture takes time, but worldwide there are already many positive examples of communities that have taken the lead. In Europe Germany and the Netherlands have become environmental leaders with flourishing recycling schemes, and in many parts of the US, legislation acts as a powerful driving force for change. Whole communities are saving and separating their waste, public awareness is rising, and innovative ways of reusing and recycling materials back into the system of production is gaining momentum. Most importantly the next generation of recyclers, the children, are receiving strong positive messages about recycling innovations from school and television. Rather than feeling powerless about the world's problems children can be highly motivated and become involved in a purposeful, active way.

But not everything is rosy. In many countries widespread opportunities to recycle post-consumer (household) waste still remain the exception rather than the rule. Facilities for recycling do vary considerably from area to area, country to country, making direct comparisons between countries difficult and sometimes inaccurate.

Collection systems are invariably more advanced in nations that have adopted waste diversion or recycling legislation for some, or most, materials. But setting recycling targets is only half the answer – encouraging manufacturers to incorporate recycled materials back into their products and getting people to buy them is the next major challenge facing the industry.

Despite the successes, there is also a backlash against recycling. This has occurred as recycling progresses from being perceived as a "good thing" to a situation where the economics have come under close scrutiny. There can be little doubt that recycling is a complex issue, since it involves resources that have to find their place in commodity markets, but its potential is often hindered by economic assessments based on short-term fiscal benefits rather than long-term environmental sustainability. So until we start questioning some of the assumptions inherent in our current economic systems, and start refining the techniques which more readily take into account the true value of goods and their full environmental impact, recycling as a means of reducing solid waste will stay as an ameliorating measure, albeit an important one, rather than an integral part of all our lives.

However there is a new sense of urgency in the need to move toward more sustainable lifestyles. The imminent threat of climate change through global warming is setting real limits on just how long the developed nations of the world can go on consuming energy and resources at their current rate. The US Environmental Protection Agency estimates that 60-65% of greenhouse gases are produced, directly and indirectly, through the consumption of energy. We must therefore rethink our policies and practices to promote energy conservation. Reducing our use of materials, including the amount that ends up as waste, and recycling (in all senses of the word) as much as we can is a vital part of such policies.

Practices

ENERGY CONSERVATION

The price we pay for energy seldom reflects the real cost of its production – the depletion of non-renewable resources such as **oil** – or the damage caused by its use. Reuse and recycling is inextricably linked with energy consumption; materials such as **glass**, **steel**, and **aluminium** are energy-intensive to manufacture. Yet if they are collected after use and reused and recycled this dramatically cuts energy consumption. For example, recycling an aluminium drinks can saves 95% of the energy that went into its original production. Not all materials will show clear-cut energy savings. Recycling organic matter – garden waste, leaves, foodstuffs – instead reduces the overall amount of waste needing disposal, and helps cut the production of **landfill gas** (methane).

   Everyone can do something to save energy. Switching off lights when not in use, buying low-energy light bulbs and energy-efficient appliances, draughtproofing your home, fitting insulation jackets to your hot water tank, showering instead of bathing, and reusing and recycling household waste are just a few energy-saving suggestions. As a guide, 1 kilowatt of electricity is equal to 1 hour of a 1-bar radiant heater, or 2 hours' ironing, or 13.5 litres (3 gallons) of hot water (UK figures).

   If you are replacing a **cooker**, **refrigerator**, freezer, or **washing machine**, remember that they are big energy-consumers. Compare the energy efficiency of new products before you buy. Look for energy labels or ask for product information. If manufacturers do not put environmental details in their brochures, think twice before buying that model. Take the time to write to the manufacturer to explain why you did not buy their product. Consumer pressure is a potent force for change. If enough people do this, manufacturers are forced to act, if they wish to remain commercially competitive.

CLOSE THE RECYCLING LOOP

There are many opportunities for reusing recycled fibres in manufacturing new products, and already many familiar, day-to-day items contain such materials, even though it is not publicized. **Cardboard** boxes, brown **envelopes**, and cereal packet cardboard are examples. Commercially recycled materials are already used in manufacturing certain types of building blocks, insulation materials, playground surfaces, roofing tiles, **carpets**, landscaping materials, office **paper**, **wallpaper**, **paint**, motor **oil**, plastic "wood", and furniture.

Industry must not get trapped into thinking that new **bottles** have to be made from **cullet**. Finding other potential uses to avoid a glut is critical, and creating new markets is one of the biggest challenges the industry has to face.

So what can individuals do? As part of the precycling ethic, consumers can actively help to promote the development of markets for recyclables by deliberately looking for, and buying, products made from reclaimed (secondary) materials. Recycling, in the true sense of the word, cannot really be considered "successful" until people are actually buying and using products that are manufactured from recycled materials.

"Closing the recycling loop" – reusing collected materials in innovative ways and as substitutes for virgin resources, is crucial if recycling programmes are to expand. It demands attention from manufacturers and consumers alike; pressure must be put on large users, such as local authorities, to make positive purchasing decisions in favour of recycled materials and provide appropriate consumer information. In the UK one paper company has been successfully promoting this idea by collecting mixed waste paper from offices, and recycling it into washroom paper towels and toilet paper, which it then sells back to the companies it collects from.

Incentives to assist further development are required. These could include: more government actions, including mandates for government procurement of recycled products, tax breaks for manufacturers who use recycled materials, levies on manufacturers who use virgin materials, and "minimum content" laws that mandate the use of recycled content in consumer products.

How such measures are actually introduced will vary considerably from country to country, but the vital issue lies in ensuring that the most appropriate do get introduced.

Along the way barriers to change may have to be altered. This is demonstrated by a situation that occurred in Los Angeles, where an ordinance (decree) to encourage the city's own heads of department to consider purchasing products with recycled content took more than two years to work its way through the city's cumbersome system. Yet officials have acknowledged that the same result could have been achieved by an executive order of the mayor in just one day. This is just one example of the many obstacles that lie en route to creating a recycling culture, and this was a city aiming to create the nation's largest kerbside recycling programme!

CONSUME LESS!

We cannot escape the fact that everything we buy creates some kind of environmental impact. But there are many ways by which we can minimize this without necessarily having to reduce our quality of life. As consumers we can exert our influence – spending power is a potent agent of social change. Refusing to buy an over-packaged item, or choosing an alternative, is our decision, but one that can force manufacturers to adopt more environmentally sound products. The well-publicized issue of CFCs in **aerosol cans** proved that. Manufacturers tend to assume that consumers prefer items made with new materials; now is the time to show them otherwise.

"Green" consumerism isn't just about consuming in a more environmentally benign manner. We must challenge the basic assumptions that we need the product in the first place. If we do, the four R's – Reduce, Reuse, Repair, and Recycle (in that order) – should come into play. An additional R, for replacing (using less-hazardous products instead), is often suggested.

DISTRICT HEATING

Converting fuel into electricity is a very wasteful process – up
to 60% of the heat is lost in steam. The answer lies in tapping
in to this wasted resource, using it to heat homes and provide
a constant supply of hot water. District heating schemes and
Combined Heat and Power (CHP) are basically recycling
techniques that benefit people and the environment. They
provide, quite literally, "heat on tap" and as individual
buildings served by such schemes do not require boilers or
open fires, air pollution is reduced. The idea is not new. By
the early 1980s, district heating already provided 30% of
Sweden's domestic heat and 55% of the CIS's requirements.
But this method of generating heat in one place and
distributing it to another has been slow to develop in other
countries. There is now a new urgency; the impact of global
warming and the need to reduce carbon dioxide emissions
from power stations means that energy policies have to be
built around energy conservation and efficiency.

LITTER

60% of litter in the developed world is discarded **packaging**,
the ubiquitous symbol of our consumer society. Global
statistics don't exist for the amount of litter that could be
recycled, but a survey in Toronto found that up to 70% of
material ending up in their litter bins was actually recyclable.
As a result the world's first recycling litter bin, with separate
compartments for **newspapers**, drinks **cans**, and **bottles**,
appeared on the streets in 1991.

But litter is not just a byproduct of society's lack of
concern; inadequate collection points and a lack of tough
action against offenders (high fines do act as a deterrent) lie
behind the worsening situation in many cities. Smokers are
said to be responsible for up to one-third of all litter.
Recycling does not prevent litter and many product labels
send out confusing messages by displaying both the
international recycling symbol (the Mobius loop, see p.30–1)
and the symbol promoting litter disposal in rubbish bins.

The impact of litter extends well beyond our urban zones.
Flytipping is widespread in rural as well as urban areas and
worldwide, marine litter – discarded nets, ropes, and **plastic**
waste – kills over 20 million seabirds every year.

Marine creatures mistakenly swallow floating **polystyrene**
and plastic fragments. A national beach clean-up in the US in
1989 recovered more than 850 tonnes of debris – 63 tonnes of
which was plastics. A survey of beached flotsam on a South
Pacific Atoll, 3000 miles from the nearest continent, found
171 **glass** and 71 plastic bottles, 25 shoes, 6 fluorescent
tubes, a toy soldier, and a car footmat.

If items are not reusable put them in the **dustbin/garbage
bin** or properly secured rubbish sack. Don't throw anything
that doesn't biodegrade into hedgerows or water.

PRECYCLING

There is no magic solution to the problem of what to do with
our waste, yet waste avoidance (waste reduction) is only now
receiving the attention it merits. But minimizing waste is far
from being a headline-grabbing issue. To overcome this the
city government of Berkeley, California, started, in 1989, to
promote the idea as "Precycling" – reinforcing the
importance of first reducing the amount of material that will
eventually need disposal, before trying to recycle the
garbage bin's contents. The main goal is to buy selectively
and to bring less potential rubbish into the home initially.

REFILL!

Refilling containers saves money and cuts **packaging** waste.
All kinds of items have the potential to be refillable.
Consumer pressure has led to refill systems now being
available for laser printer cartridges. Many **paper** recycling
collectors offer this complementary service for workplaces. It
costs about 40% less to refill a cartridge than to buy a new
one, and they can be refilled between 3 and 6 times before
having to be scrapped.

Some refill options only start to become truly economic when the item is returned several times. Bottles fall into this category. Incentives such as deposits (money back on return) do motivate the consumer to return containers, but some systems, such as doorstep milk delivery in the UK, have worked well without these. Because returnable bottles are made with thicker glass, overall energy savings only start to be made when the bottles are refilled several times. In theory a glass milk bottle can be reused up to 30 times before it is sent for recycling.

Try to buy refillable items in preference to others – an increasing number of household cleaning and personal care products are stocked in refills. In its efforts to adopt a "green" mantle, the detergent industry has now veered toward encouraging consumers to buy larger, minimally-packed refill packs, yet refilling, along with bulk-buying, has long been an option in wholefood stores. Keep large **glass jars** and bottles, tins with lids, and **plastic** containers for this purpose. Make sure you label containers and do not refill bottles that have contained chemicals.

REUSE!

The reuse of materials is a traditional skill and still forms the basis of many of the oldest industries. But too many products today are not designed or constructed with reuse in mind. Mixed materials that are hard to separate, or impossible to distinguish, are common, and even if reuse is an option, the local set-up (collection/return facilities) may mitigate against it. Instead materials end up in the dustbin/garbage bin or on the scrap heap.

Why reuse? Beyond the issue of saving resources, and often non-renewable ones, the energy-saving implications can be very significant. But reuse is not just something to be done at the household level. Industries both large and small are involved in remanufacturing throughout the world. Reuse of scrap **steel** in manufacturing processes recaptures the benefits of energy already expended at only a fraction of the original energy expenditure. The World Bank estimates that for every kilowatt-hour of energy spent in remanufacturing, between 4 and 5 kilowatt hours are recovered.

Reconditioning is a form of reuse that is frequently applied to **cars**, **refrigerators**, **washing machines**, and other household appliances (see **White goods**). It could be argued that by extending the life of an older machine, a less energy-efficient appliance is kept in operation, thus wasting resources. While this is true, market acceptance of products tends to decide whether products will be remanufactured. If a product is grossly inefficient (consuming large amounts of energy) it is unlikely to receive this treatment.

REPAIR

Repair is an integral part of the recycling ethic. There are many options: rebuilding, renewing, reviving, recovering, recreating, restoring, refurbishing, reconditioning, and redecorating. At the heart of all these lies the eventual aim to reuse materials rather than disposing of them.

Repair, as well as regular maintenance, extends the life of many common items including **tools**, appliances, vehicles **shoes**, **clothing**, and **office equipment**.

Second-hand no longer means second best. Refurbishment/repair workshops take items apart, clean or recondition them, and reassemble for resale. The most commonly sought-after goods are furniture, **bicycles**, and electrical items. Furniture renovation projects generally find that demand is already high and exceeds supply. Such projects divert volumes of bulky furniture away from the waste stream and keep usable materials out of **landfill**. Additionally, they prevent a waste of human potential by offering skills training.

RECYCLING SYMBOLS

Worldwide there is a wide variety of recycling symbols, trade marks, and logos in use. Emerging eco-labelling schemes are an attempt to reduce confusion and misleading claims. Consumers must have easy access to accurate information regarding the environmental impact of any product.

There are several misleading terms in common usage that need defining. Just because a product is "recyclable" it is not necessarily benign. It would be helpful if manufacturers listed what materials they used. The term is often used on plastics and cartons when collection systems are not widely available. "Environmentally friendly" suggests that products are harmless to the environment. Very few consumer products have no negative environmental impact. The word "biodegradable" is frequently used on products that have always been biodegradable, such as detergents. The real question is how long substances take to break down - days, weeks, or years? Biodegradable plastics disintegrate into tiny pieces, they do not disappear altogether. "Recycled content" can vary from small percentages of preconsumer, or mill, waste to 100% postconsumer waste.

The Mobius Loop is the most used (and misused) symbol signifying the reuse and recycling of materials. The three arrows represent solids, liquids, and gases, and also the three stages of recycling: collection, production into new recycled products and packaging, and consumer recognition of the role of recycling. The symbol is only supposed to be used on goods that are "recyclable" or include "recycled content"

3

1. Green Dot
2. Battery return symbol
3. Mobius Loop
4. Blue Angel
5. Environmental Choice Programme
6. Ecomark
7. Nordic Environmental label
8. Aluminium Can Recycling Association
9. European Ecolabel

1

NH-VT
Solid Waste
Project
1•603•543•1201

2

The Blue Angel (Germany) was the world's first eco-label (1987). Over 3000 products in 57 product categories carry the label. Various paper products have to contain 100% recycled paper to qualify for the label

4

The Environmental Choice Programme (Canada). Manufacturers apply for the logo if their products meet criteria set out by the ECB. A full environmental impact assessment, including raw materials, energy usage, and ultimate disposal is necessary for each product category. A public review process allows further improvements to be incorporated. Products include those that increase energy efficiency, reduce hazardous wastes, use recycled materials, and facilitate reuse

The European Ecolabel was launched to avoid a proliferation of separate national schemes. Award of the label signals that the item meets "rigorous environmental criteria and proper fitness for use"

The Green Dot indicates that the packaging will be collected under the German Duales system

The Ecomark (Japan) This is based on the Blue Angel scheme, but only distinguishes products that cause less harm to the environment. It does not attempt to set standards for quality. Product categories include books and magazines made from recycled papers, compost makers, and CFC-free aerosols

6

7

5

8

9

INSIDE YOUR CUPBOARD

Packaging is used to wrap most of the items found in the kitchen store cupboard and there is no ideal form of packaging: every material creates some environmental impact. Manufacturers can choose to avoid the use or production of certain packaging types or can try to create the possibility for reuse and recycling. Support those who are doing something to reduce waste and lobby supermarkets to provide recycling facilities.

Precycle! Cut your weekly waste by as much as 20% by careful choice of packaging. Look for products with the least packaging. Choose recyclable materials - glass, paper, cardboard, steel, and aluminium have established collection systems. **Refill!** Bulk-buy items you use frequently (nuts, flour, cereals and cleaning detergents). Use glass jars or ceramic containers for storage.

1. Boxed cling film/plastic wrap, aluminium foil, rubbish bags
2. Boxed foodstuffs
3. Egg cartons
4. Steel food cans
5. Juice cartons
6. Glass bottles and jars
7. Drinks cans
8. Wrapped toilet rolls
9. Shrink-wrapped food on plastic foam trays

Avoid! Do not buy packages made from two or more different materials, for example cartons with an inner layer of plastic and aluminium. Laminates are difficult to recycle. Avoid using clingfilm/plastic wrap as it is difficult to wash and reuse. Use long-lasting food containers or wrap in greaseproof paper instead.
Choose! Buy products such as honey in glass jars, not plastic tubes.

Return! Take milk and beer bottles and egg cartons back for refilling.
Separate at source! Keep steel and aluminium cans apart so that they can be recycled.
Save for new uses! Cut down large cereal boxes to use as magazine holders or give them to children's play projects for making junk models.

Wash and squash! Discarded aluminium cans can be reprocessed into new cans, saving 95% of the energy used to make them.

SEPARATE AT SOURCE

Separating waste at source, in the home or workplace, is one
of the most cost-effective ways of giving waste a value. An
aluminium can discarded in the dustbin/garbage bin is
worth nothing, but separated out it has a value – about one
penny (UK) – and is in demand by the aluminium industry.

If waste isn't separated, mixed non-organic materials
generally have little value unless the waste disposal authority
has separation techniques (e.g. magnetic steel extraction) or
disposes of its waste through **incineration** with energy
recovery. Technologies for separating certain types of
plastic bottles (PET) using lasers do exist in a few plastic
recovery schemes (material from **bottle banks** or kerbside
collection), but at one million pounds per machine their
adoption is very limited. Therefore sorting at processing
plants is often done manually.

Removing more reusable waste from the dustbin/garbage
bin depends on the consumer. A lack of information about
what can be recycled, confusing labelling on products, and
not enough accessible recycling facilities all hamper
materials' reclamation.

Getting into the 4 Rs habit (reduce, reuse, repair, recycle)
takes time, especially where the systems are voluntary.
Location can be a hindrance – in urban areas more attention
is now being given to systems for apartment dwellers.
Distances from recycling facilities can be a problem, too.

Action at National Level

CONSUMER INFORMATION

Information is the key to change. Without it the consumer cannot reflect or react and make changes.

In the world of recycling the most recognizable symbol is the three-arrowed triangle, the Mobius Loop (see p.30–1). It appears on recycled **paper**, on **packaging**, drinks **cans**, and even on disposable cups, and like the accompanying wording "recyclable" or "recycled content", the symbol is open to much abuse (see pp.30–1).

According to a UK marketing study, the boom of so-called "green" products and packaging has failed to become an important influence in most consumers' purchasing decisions. One reason is that consumer confusion is rife – many people cannot distinguish between the terms "recycled" and "recyclable", and puzzle over what "recycled content" actually means.

ECO-LABELLING

The original aim behind eco-labelling schemes was to provide guidance to the consumer about which products had less of an overall impact on the environment. However, as countries have devised and publicized their schemes, eco-labelling as a concept has proved to be very contentious. In order critically to assess all the possible environmental impacts a product's manufacture, use, and disposal may have on the environment, judgements have to be made – even though some of the impacts are unquantified, or even unquantifiable. Life-cycle analysis (LCA) is one technique now gaining worldwide recognition, but dissent on how to measure the "cradle to grave" impact of a product is likely to continue. Some critics argue that LCA studies always seem to come out in favour of the company that sponsored them!

The world's first eco-labelling scheme was the German Blue Angel. Although this is now criticized for its shortcomings, it has provided useful lessons for other countries, and the EC, in drawing up its Community-wide scheme. In marketing terms there is undoubtedly much to be gained from the award of an eco-label, or the word "recycled" or "recyclable" on a product.

DESIGN, FOR RECYCLING

Making waste reduction happen means challenging the status quo; re-evaluating the usefulness of products, asking questions about their environmental impact, questioning whether alternatives exist, and promoting the "less is best" concept as widely as possible.

As a positive example of retailers taking the lead, one supermarket chain in Zurich started a campaign in the late 1980s to reduce **packaging**, increase recycling, and cut its energy consumption. The most appropriate materials for products were substituted – **paper** in place of **plastic** wrappings for bread, polypropylene plastic instead of **aluminium** foil for chocolate bars. **Aerosol cans** were abandoned in favour of gravity pumps that did not contain harmful propellant gases, and throughout the store customers were urged to buy refills and bulk purchases.

Help eliminate over-packaged goods from your shopping basket. Put pressure on manufacturers to reduce complex, multi-material packaging. Letters do count. Congratulate them when they produce waste-reducing packaging, urge them to extend this to other ranges, and complain bitterly when marketing ploys to sell products have little consideration for the consumer's ability to reuse or recycle the packaging.

HOUSEHOLD HAZARDOUS WASTE

Potentially hazardous household waste includes any material disposed of by a household that could pose a risk to human health or the environment, due to its chemical or biological nature. Such wastes include: paint and related products;

motoring products; cleaning agents; pharmaceuticals; water treatment chemicals; garden products (pesticides, wood preservatives, herbicides); pet products; other household items including fluorescent tubes, **batteries**, and smoke alarms. Some products used in repair work can be toxic.

Categorizing wastes in this way is not just a scare tactic. Many substances in common use can cause problems if they are dumped or poured down the drain. In the US a reminder about this hazard can be found beside roadside drains.

Another very real problem for large-scale composting schemes is the amount of various substances, including **heavy metals**, which end up in **compost**. These problems are leading industry carefully to scrutinize where the waste comes from.

INDUSTRIAL WASTE

Many industrial processes already reuse production (pre-consumer) waste not necessarily on environmental grounds but for economy. In steel-making, some proportion of scrap is always used because it drastically cuts energy costs. Recycling at source also happens within the **paper** and **plastics** industry. Nor is production waste routinely re-routed back into manufacturing processes. Treating this on site and reusing it is a practical option if it does not contain toxic materials that necessitate separate handling.

Moving toward more sustainable systems of production demands waste minimization and investigation of the options of recycling post-consumer materials. One way of reducing industrial wastes is to use them for another product. For example, construction and demolition waste is usually expensive to transport to disposal sites. Yet if it is crushed it becomes an ideal material for road bases and other projects.

Another way to stimulate recycling is by waste exchange schemes, where "waste" materials from one industrial process become the raw material for another. Companies can advertise materials they need to dispose of and can request materials as well.

BERKELEY: RECYCLING COMMUNITY

Seventeen percent of Berkeley's waste is recycled and 50% of recyclable material is collected for reuse, remanufacture, and recycling. State legislation in California demands a 25% reduction in the waste stream by 1995, rising to 50% by 2000. Waste-reducing measures include minimum standards for recycled glass – bottles must contain at least 15% cullet, increasing to 65% cullet content by 2005. 25% of newspapers (50% by 1995) must contain recycled paper.

What comes in?
• Unwanted household items such as white goods, appliances, and furniture
• Recyclable items for reprocessing such as newspapers, glass bottles, and plastic bottles
• Items for safe disposal such as batteries
• Organics such as backyard waste, scrap timber, grass clippings, and leaves

What goes out?
• Household items in good condition such as bric-a-brac, white goods, cutlery, records, furniture, electrical appliances, scrap wood
• Cullet, newspapers, and cardboard for reprocessing
• Composted material
• Batteries and car products for safe disposal

Recycling Centre
• Private hauliers and individuals bring in materials from the commercial waste stream, including glass, paper, cardboard, and aluminium.
• Individuals bring in newspapers. While 50% is exported to Asia, some is sent to de-inking plants for reuse in new products.
• Mixed cullet is collected for the reprocessing market. Only 5% of glass beer bottles and 7.5% of soft drink bottles are refillable in the US.
• Recycling aluminium is highly profitable. Cans are sold for processing into aluminium sheeting. Some metal is exported. Unofficial totters salvage cans.
• Bales of cardboard are collected for reprocessing into new boxes.
• PET plastic is bought from recyclers by a plastics company. 50% is exported, the rest is sent for reprocessing.
• Compostibles are chipped, shredded, and composted. Households are encouraged to undertake home composting.

RECYCLING ROUTES: GLASS

Glass is not biodegradable and can be constantly remelted and remoulded into new products, without losing its quality. So separate all glass bottles and jars from the rest of your waste and recycle them. Throwing glass into the dustbin/garbage bin means that it ends up in landfill sites or is incinerated.

• Deposit legislation ensures that bottles are returned to the store, dairy, or brewery. This route saves the most energy and raw materials
• Recyclable glass is taken to a bottle bank and cullet is sent for remelting into new bottles, saving some energy and resources
• Kerbside collectors take glass for processing into new bottles
• Bottles thrown into the dustbin/garbage bin are either landfilled or incinerated

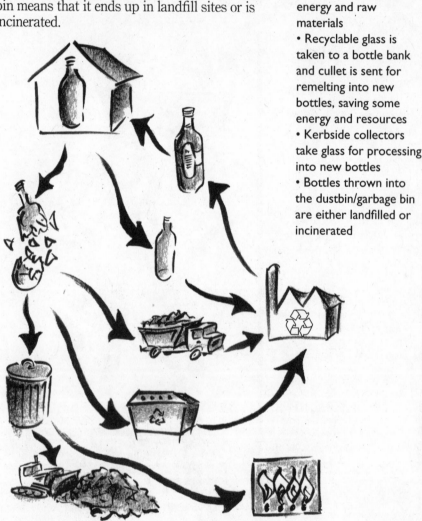

RECYCLING ROUTES: CANS

The most common can recovery systems are can banks and kerbside collections. Aluminium fetches a much higher scrap value than steel, so it is preferable to separate at source (test with a magnet - if it sticks the can is made from steel). Some can banks accept both types of can, separation occurs at the processing plant with magnetic extraction. After separation and shredding, tin is removed from the steel. The steel is compressed into bales and sold to the steel-making industry. Aluminium is sent for remelting and manufacture into new aluminium products.

- Cans are taken to can banks or collected by kerbside collection
- Cans are reprocessed into new cans
- Cans thrown into the dustbin/garbage bin are either landfilled or incinerated
- Sackfuls are collected by charities and community groups

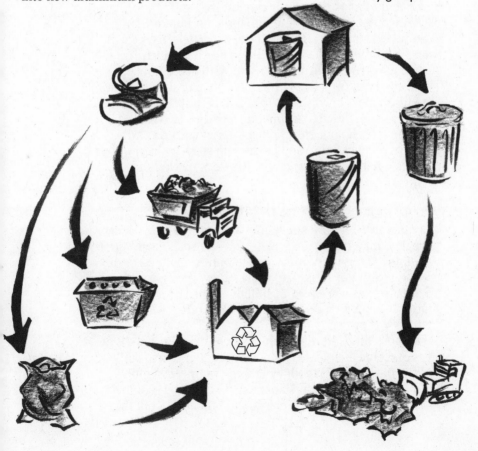

LEGISLATION

Legislation on waste reduction and recycling varies considerably from country to country. Generally more materials are collected in places where legislation exists, but this doesn't necessarily make the recycling rate higher. Legislation may lead in the US, but finding end markets for the reclaimed products continues to be a problem.

Legislation tends to define and ban environmentally unacceptable goods, rather than promoting "clean products". In Denmark, non-returnable containers are banned, and Sweden uses a deposit system on items, including **cars**, to encourage recovery for scrap. Germany has set stringent new standards for recyclable **packaging**, and France has a packaging decree that came into force on January 1 1993.

Some US states ban the disposal of garden/backyard waste in rubbish collections, others ban it in **landfills**, and in certain parts of California the use of **polystyrene** is banned. The European Community has passed a number of relevant directives, most of which have still to be implemented by member countries. These include a ban on **batteries** containing high concentrations of **heavy metals** and a directive on packaging and packaging waste, which will place new responsibilities on manufacturers and retailers.

WORKPLACE RECYCLING SCHEMES

Increasingly there are substantial opportunities to recover separated materials from business waste streams. In the UK over 130,000 tonnes of office waste **paper** could be economically recovered and recycled every year. And in the US, businesses use about 21 million tonnes every year – yet studies have shown that about 70% of all office waste could have been recycled.

The possibilities for new alternatives exist in every type of business. One analysis in the US found that restaurant waste is 37% paper and 36% food, while in a commercial office building 65% of the rubbish appears to be paper, compared to 50% from education and government offices. Within the construction industry 33% of construction debris was wood waste with 27% of inert material and "fines" – ash and dust.

Knowing where to start is often the first stumbling block. A few small-scale recycling practices that work and perhaps save company money are far better than trying to recycle everything and giving up after a few months.

Reduce your waste by getting hold of the right information. Many environmental groups supply relevant literature, and trade groups may offer promotional material and even collection sacks. Government information might be helpful, too, particularly for incentives to cut waste.

Maximize energy and resource savings by making reuse the next best option to reduce. It many seem obvious that discarded photocopying paper or one-sided draft reports are ideal for scrap paper, but many offices throw this material away. Breaking the habit of reaching for a new sheet of paper for every message or draft letter is difficult. Getting workplaces to choose the right grade of paper for the right use is important too – why use top-quality stationery for internal telephone messages or memos? Recycle materials that cannot be reused. Before collecting anything, check that there is an end market for it. Some materials, such as **aluminium cans**, high-quality office paper, and computer listings fetch a high scrap value and are always in demand. Such paper can be used as a direct subsitute for wood pulp in the paper-making process, saving raw materials and reducing pollution. But thermal fax paper should not be included, the coating prevents recycling.

Unwanted office equipment or furniture is always needed by charities and not-for-profit groups. As part of the recycling loop make sure your company is opting for positive purchasing policies in favour of items like recycled paper for stationery and photocopiers. Recycled paper is often cited as the culprit for jamming photocopiers – often a myth, so seek advice from suppliers. Washroom products – including toilet paper and towels should be made from recycled paper, preferably unbleached.

Processes

BIODEGRADABLE MATERIALS

This term applies to materials that are capable of being broken down into their constituent parts by micro-organisms and bacteria. A familiar example in nature is the annual fall of leaves – one of the earth's great recycling processes, which releases nutrients back into the soil.

Composting (see **Compost**) is a practice that demonstrates just how biodegradable some items are. Uneaten food, garden/backyard waste, even small quantities of **newspaper**, will break down to produce a rich, friable compost in a relatively short time.

"Green consumerism" has unfortunately led to many inaccurate claims about the environmental impact of products and their **packaging**. The word "biodegradable" on a package may not mean much since all organic materials eventually break down or change their chemical composition. The real question is how long does this take and what will the detrimental environmental impacts be? A classic example is **detergent**. Most detergents have long been biodegradable, yet phosphate-packed products, which often contain added cleaning agents, chemicals, and optical whiteners can legitimately make the same claims over biodegradability as manufacturers who use only natural soaps, kaolin clay, and essential oils in their products. Environmentally the best substances are those that degrade within a matter of days rather than weeks or months.

Discarded rubbish takes far longer to break down. The Office of Recycling, State of Rhode Island, US, states that a traffic ticket probably takes between two and four weeks to degrade, a wool sock one year, a painted wooden stake 13 years, an **aluminium** can between 200 and 500 years, and a **glass** bottle an indefinite period of time.

COLLECTION SYSTEMS

Legislation lies behind many collection systems. In some countries the collection of certain materials is mandatory; elsewhere a voluntary system exists. There are advantages and disadvantages to both systems, complicated by different tax systems which usually favour raw materials instead of recycled. The vagaries of supply and demand are another drawback, particularly for the lower grades of paper.

There are two main options for collection of recyclable materials – bring systems, where householders or traders take waste to a collection point, and kerbside collection, where separated or co-mingled recyclables are collected directly from households.

Collection cost per tonne of domestic waste is seen as one of the biggest stumbling blocks to meeting recycling targets. Charging for the actual amount collected, whether from business or from homes, is a system that can lead to waste reduction. In Seattle householders sign up with a garbage collector for collecting a certain-sized bin each week. If they have more waste than this they have to buy a "trash tag" to ensure their extra bag of waste is collected. As the costs rise steeply the more waste that is generated, this acts as a real incentive to partipating in kerbside recycling collections.

"Bring" systems — Familiar examples include **bottle banks**, can banks, containers for collecting **plastic** bottles, and specialized collection facilities such as separate bins for **batteries** and other items containing hazardous substances.

The onus is on the consumer to take materials to recycling centres, local authority civic amenity sites, or to collection banks on the streets and in supermarket car parks. Although "bring" systems generally collect less material, they are cheaper to operate than door-to-door kerbside collection. Evidence demonstrates that the higher the density of banks, the more people are likely to support them.

Buy-back schemes — On cost grounds **aluminium** buy-back programmes, where collectors are paid for the amount of **cans** they collect or bring in to redemption centres, can be justified.

Deposit refund schemes — By encouraging consumers to return items, usually beverage containers and especially **bottles**, to retailers after use for refilling, deposit refund schemes have been effective in supporting recycling. More countries are again looking at reintroducing this option.

Green bin system — Keeping wet organic waste – hence the name "green" bin – separate from dry wastes such as **paper**, **glass**, and metals was a system pioneered in Germany and the Netherlands. Another option, a split bin, with compartments, serves the same function in keeping compostible waste away from unrecyclable items including disposables, and separate from returnable packaging.

There are variations on this system. In Frankfurt the brown Biobin is issued to householders for putrescible waste that could be composted. Their success is very dependent on householder's participation in separating materials, plus a strong demand for the compost.

Kerbside collection — The first scheme for collecting a range of separated recyclables from outside peoples' homes started in Ontario. In existence now for over a decade the Canadian "Blue Box" system has become a role model for other similar collections throughout the world. Although the economics of kerbside collection, and particularly the Blue Box system, is currently the subject of much debate, and early pilot schemes have been abandoned or modified, the general aim remains to achieve higher recovery rates of recyclables, and to keep reusable materials out of **landfill** and **incineration**. In reality it is vital to have some element of kerbside collection in order to achieve recycling targets.

Incentives — Switching to waste reduction and recycling programmes at the nationwide level ultimately depends on a number of levers, including incentives, to make things happen. There are many critics ready to say that recycling is not economic; in the short term this can often be true, the economics are complicated and tax systems rule in favour of raw materials, not recycled, fibres. For example, in the US users of virgin raw materials receive a tax credit, making it cheaper to use new materials.

Governments often admit that market forces alone are insufficient to ensure an optimum level of recycling. Establishing viable collections and creating new markets for recycled goods takes time. Incentives can help this process along. These will vary in effectiveness from country to country, but the potential range of economic instruments to stimulate recycling includes: product charges; raw materials charge; deposit refund schemes; waste collection charges; waste disposal charges; transferable recycling targets; changing responsibilities; direct subsidies; tax concessions; removal of tax allowances; market support schemes; preferential purchase systems that discriminate in favour of goods with recycled content.

It is desirable that legal instruments as well as financial incentives are promoted together to achieve a regulatory effect. Levies on products do not encourage waste minimization as much as a levy on the primary material.

Selective deposits, combined with legal requirements, are another option for certain products such as cars. Such a scheme to encourage reclamation is already under way.

ENERGY FROM WASTE
Plastic, **paper**, and **rags** release a substantial amount of energy when burned; energy-from-waste schemes trap this to produce electricity or steam as a useful byproduct. **Incineration** with energy recovery is an essential part of many countries' waste-disposal strategies. In the US 122 facilities were operating in 1991, generating enough electricity to power 1.2 million households. Nearly one-quarter of Japan's waste is burned in energy-from-waste schemes, and Germany now burns over 30% of its non-recyclable waste.

This method is not without its critics. Incinerators are costly to build and strict pollution control procedures are necessary as burning wastes can create **dioxins** and other undesirable hazardous substances. Energy-from-waste/

INSIDE YOUR DUSTBIN/GARBAGE BIN

Municipal waste is varied: the proportions of different materials reflect different lifestyles, so the contents of a typical household dustbin/garbage bin vary from country to country. Access to recycling facilities, kerbside collections, and legislation are important factors in keeping recyclables out of the dustbin/garbage bin. But culture and poverty also play a significant role.

Comparing the international nature of waste is far from easy. Publicly available information is limited and statistics may, or may not, include recyclables diverted away from solid waste. Many countries are beginning to develop programmes for keeping certain types of organic matter (e.g. garden/backyard waste) out of the dustbin/garbage bin. Many US states ban such matter from general waste collection.

Typical French household waste (by % weight)
Paper/cardboard 33%
Putrescible material 23%
Glass 10%
Metal 6%
Plastic 10%
Textiles 3%
Fines (ash) 10%
Miscellaneous 5%

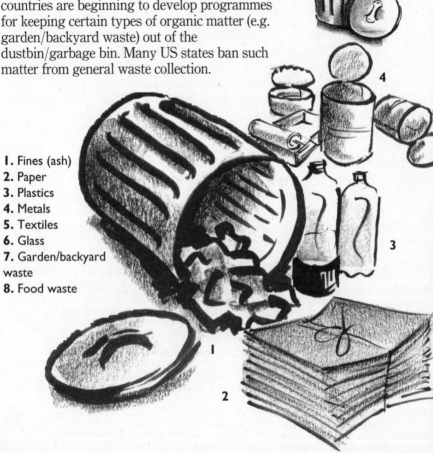

1. Fines (ash)
2. Paper
3. Plastics
4. Metals
5. Textiles
6. Glass
7. Garden/backyard waste
8. Food waste

Typical US household waste (by % weight)
Paper/cardboard 40%
Plastics 8%
Textiles 11%
Metals 8.3%
Glass 7%
Yard waste 17.3%
Food waste 7.4%
Source: Environmental Protection Agency 1989

Typical Australian household waste (by % weight)
Putrescible material 41%
Paper/cardboard 18.7%
Glass 12.9%
Plastics 7.3%
Composite materials 5.7%
Metals 5.3%
Miscellaneous 8.6%
Source: Tasmanian Recycling and Litter Awareness Council 1991

Typical UK household waste (by % weight)
Paper/cardboard 33%
Plastics 7%
Textiles 4%
Metals 8%
Glass 10%
Organics 20%
Fines (ash) 10%
Other 8%
Source: SWAP 1991

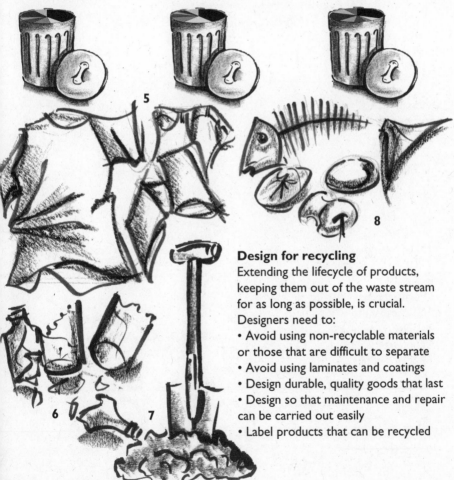

Design for recycling

Extending the lifecycle of products, keeping them out of the waste stream for as long as possible, is crucial. Designers need to:
• Avoid using non-recyclable materials or those that are difficult to separate
• Avoid using laminates and coatings
• Design durable, quality goods that last
• Design so that maintenance and repair can be carried out easily
• Label products that can be recycled

THE WASTE WATER CYCLE

A constant supply of clean drinking water is taken for granted in all the industrialized nations, but every day vast quantities are wasted by inefficient processes. A single toilet flush uses 10 litres (2 gallons) of water; one average bath uses 80-90 litres (20 gallons); one shower uses 30 litres (6.5 gallons); one washing machine load uses up to 100 litres (22 gallons) - depending on wash type and machine model - and one dishwasher load uses 50 litres (11 gallons). The US uses over 70 times more water per person than Ghana, and over four times more than the average Swiss resident.

Water usage in the average home
1. Bath
2. Toilet and cistern
3. Shower
4. Household sinks and taps
5. Washing machine (front loader)
6. Dishwasher
7. Jug water filter
8. Kettle
9. Garden sprinkler
10. Water butt
11. Drip sprinkler
12. Mulch
13. Garden tap

Garden
Garden sprinklers use over 910 litres (200 gallons) an hour. Buy a special sensor which shuts off the water once the soil is moist. Collect rain water in a butt and use a watering can, or reuse bath water. Use wood chips or bark shavings as a mulch to retain moisture in the soil. Greywater systems, which collect and reuse household wastewater are forbidden in many places due to fears of contamination. But bath water and tap water is reusable. Water purification, using plants as pollution filters, is integral to greywater systems.

Sewage
Toilet waste and washing machine water must go into the mains sewerage system.

Kitchen

Mend dripping taps - a steady drip can lose 90 litres (20 gallons) a day. Washing machines consume 12% of a home's water use. Front loaders use 40% less water than top loaders. Run machines with a full load, lower the water temperature to save energy and use the economy button. Use a dishwasher once a day, not after every meal. When peeling vegetables use a bowl rather than running the tap. Fit low-flow controls or aerators to taps.

Bathroom

Between 65 and 75% of the indoor water we use every day flows through the bathroom. Flushing the toilet is the biggest domestic water user. Install a low-flush or dual-flush cistern, which cuts water use by 50%. Or put in a toilet dam. Mend cistern leaks. A daily shower rather than a bath saves about 420 litres (92 gallons) a week. Install water-saving showerheads, using up to 70% less water. Share bath water or reuse it to water plants or wash the car. Don't run the tap when brushing teeth.

incineration is not regarded as true recycling by many
organizations because materials are destroyed for ever
(although post-incineration steel can be recovered by
magnetic extraction). But when waste is too mixed or
contaminated, or if markets are poor for a low-grade material
energy-from-waste can be a desirable alternative to dumping
potentially useful materials in the ground.

HIGH-GRADE VERSUS LOW-GRADE RECYCLING

The most desirable, both environmentally and economically,
is when recycling processes create products of comparable,
or only slightly lowered, quality to the original. An obvious
example of high-grade recycling is aluminium, which can be
recycled again and again without losing any of its properties.
But the real benefits lie in the tremendous energy savings.
For example, up to 95% of the original energy input can be
saved by utilizing **aluminium** scrap. **Glass** is another
example of high-grade recycling.

OXFAM WASTESAVER

Reuse and recycling materials lies at the heart of Oxfam's
Wastesaver scheme in the UK. Money from the sale of
processed textiles and **aluminium** funds Oxfam's
development work abroad. A true example of creating wealth
from waste. A network of high street stores collects
unwanted items of **clothing**, bric-a-brac, **aluminium cans**,
and foil. Clothing too damaged to be resold in the shops is
sent to the Wastesaver factory. Here it is sorted into different
grades: "usables" are sent abroad to refugees, while the rest
is separated for reprocessing. White cottons and woollens
are reused by the textile trade; the rest is made into
industrial wiping rags, or sold to the furniture industry for
manufacture into **carpet** underlay and roofing felt, or as a
stuffing material. In 1988-9 over 10,000 tonnes of textiles
were processed.

POLLUTION

Pollution disrupts, poisons, and prevents the natural cycles of life. Yet daily we continue activities that worsen the situation. In our environment, in the air we breathe, and in the food we eat, is evidence of a consumer-driven society out of control.

Pollution is frequently a byproduct of economic activity, yet this should not mean that strict controls cannot be enforced to reduce its effects. Waste minimization techniques and recycling can help. Producing an **aluminium** drinks **cans** from aluminium scrap rather than from virgin ore cuts emissions of nitrogen oxides by 95% and sulphur dioxide emissions by 99% – both major contributors to acid rain. Recycling waste **paper** can cut air pollution by 75% as can buying longer-lasting and energy-efficient items.

Closer to home, the materials we use for building and furnishing our homes contribute to pollution. Treating new fabrics with formaldehyde reduces the need for ironing, but vapours are slowly released into the indoor environment and have been shown to cause allergic reactions. Lighting a bonfire liberates potentially hazardous substances from treated **wood**, old paintwork, and some types of **plastic**.

While pollution is a global problem, some solutions can only begin at local level. Individual actions may seem insignificant, but collectively they can have a real influence.

PRE- AND POSTCONSUMER WASTE

Distinctions have to be made when comparing recycling processes, and their economics. Preconsumer waste is production waste or factory scrap. Uncontaminated with other materials it can be fed straight back into the production system, resulting in high-quality goods. **Plastics** and steel shavings are routinely recycled in this manner.

Postconsumer waste is domestic waste. Separating for recycling is more difficult, especially for laminated **packaging** and plastics. "Closing the recycling loop" (see p.24), by encouraging more manufacturers to incorporate postconsumer materials into their products, is important.

RECYCLING

This is the process of putting "waste" back into the system of production and consumption. Reuse is the best form of recycling. When this is not possible, reclaimed materials can be substituted or processed as the raw materials for another product. Overall, recycling is just one route to taking a more responsible and sustainable approach to how we use the earth's resources.

Because there is no standardized system for measuring waste, or the inputs and outputs of recycling processes, or even a standard definition of the different types of waste, comparisons of recycling rates between countries is difficult.

But recycling is not just about collection; creating strong markets for the end product is vital. Precycling, refilling, recharging, revamping, recovering, restoring, and repairing items are all essential parts of the recycling ethic.

RENEWABLE RESOURCES

These are resources that are replenished biologically within a relatively short time span, compared with non-renewable resources, which are only renewed over geological time spans. **Wood** is a renewable resource – trees grow, are harvested, and replanted. But products made from **plastics** are based on a non-renewable resource – petroleum **oil**. Many metals are only present within the earth's crust in limited quantities. These include, **iron**, copper, **lead**, **silver**, **tin**, and **zinc**.

Putting a price on renewable resources is difficult. Life Cycle Analysis is one technique for assessing environmental impact, but there remain many unanswered questions about measuring the unquantifiables. How do you judge the renewability of timber from well-managed woods against non-renewable oil reserves? Too many simplified claims are made without consideration of whether the product is based on renewable, as opposed to finite, resources.

RESOURCE RECOVERY PLANTS

A general term for any method of reclaiming materials or
energy from municipal waste. In the US this includes
facilities that burn municipal waste – either in its original
form or in pellets as refuse-derived fuel, to produce electricity
or steam. In recycling terms, minimizing waste at source is
the cheapest way of protecting dwindling resources and
cutting the amount of rubbish needing disposal. Consumer
pressure on manufacturers to reduce complex **packaging**
and to use only single recyclable materials is worth while.

SCHOOLS, RECYCLING COLLECTIONS

Schools reuse many materials in art and craft projects – rolls
of **paper**, **card**, colour **magazines**, fabric scraps, textile
samples, **wallpaper** pattern books, **cardboard** boxes,
discarded **jewellery**, beads, **buttons**, and **aluminium foil**.
Newspaper is the main ingredient of papier mâché. But as
well as reusing things for fun, many schools are actively
involved in collecting materials for recycling. Stamps and
milk bottle tops are the old favourites for fundraising, but
collections of aluminium and **steel** drinks **cans** are
encouraged by the reclamation trade. Schools receive
promotional videos, badges, and collection sacks.

If you are connected with a school, investigate the
possibilities of setting up or expanding a recycling collection.
Or you could start by raising awareness; compiling a
recycling guide to local facilities for reuse, repair, and
recycling is something that could give your school good
publicity. These directories are positive ways of showing
people how to reuse everyday items and demonstrate just
how much has an alternative use. Approach sympathetic
local businesses for donations toward the cost of printing, or
ask them to supply the paper. Recycling is very much a
collaborative venture, so exploit all the opportunities you can.

Before collecting anything, work out where you are going
to store it, check fire regulations for paper goods, and find
out who is going to collect or buy it from your school.

The WORLD of RECYCLING

" *We must learn to think globally and in a long-term perspective.*"
Gro Harlem
Brundtland

This section takes a snapshot glance at some of the reuse and recycling practices around the world. Information about schemes is constantly changing as waste minimization and recycling gain a greater foothold in some countries' economies. Some elements, such as salvage and re-utilization of materials, will continue to be a necessity born out of a lack of natural resources, insufficient access to them, or poverty. It is almost impossible to compare statistics of recycling rates in different countries since countries classify their wastes in different ways. Some countries do not include certain types of waste within their national statistics, while others weigh only a small proportion of their total waste or weigh it in different ways. Some do not consider certain materials to be within their classification of waste. It is also misleading to compare countries that have very different collection and recycling rates as a result of national policies and legislation.

Providing a very general picture of certain practices does, however, provide a sense of what can and what cannot be achieved and demonstrates that recycling is a fast-growing industrial activity. On the more negative side it should be remembered that although some countries, usually in the developing world, seem to be relatively efficient in reclaiming and recycling materials, there is often a threat to health through contact with untreated water or waste, through inadequate controls over the dumping of hazardous waste, and through dangerous reprocessing practices.

AFRICA

With a population of 642 million (1990) Africa not only faces an enormous problem in finding enough food for its rapidly growing population (per capita grain production is falling, leading to greater reliance on imports) but also in finding a solution to the growing problem of solid waste disposal. In most of the major cities rubbish is simply collected and dumped on any available land. Few environmental regulations exist and so it is common to find all types of waste, including hazardous materials, at such sites. This can endanger the health of people who scour the dumps. The main problem is that there is no co-ordinated programme for waste disposal and decision-makers have been accused of having an "out of sight, out of mind" mentality.

Lax controls have also meant that other countries and transnational companies have used parts of Africa as dumping grounds for their own toxic materials.

Composting techniques have traditionally been used to dispose of certain wastes, and programmes exist in Tanzania, Kenya, Nigeria, and Botswana for dealing with **nightsoil**.

Uncollected waste can be a health hazard as well as a nuisance. Not all **plastic** is reused and in Njamena, Chad, the dry climate inhibits the natural rotting of materials.

Small-scale funding from Oxfam has allowed old **oil** drums to be converted by local blacksmiths into dustbins/garbage bins for an organized waste collection.

Creative reuse of materials includes metal wire for making children's toys and decorative items, drinks **cans** cut down to make oil lamps, shoe soles fashioned from discarded car **tyres**, and hats knitted from plastic-bag "yarn". The ubiquitous drinks **can** is even found in use as a roofing material and for building goat pens in Damaraland, Namibia.

Reliance on inadequate supplies of water has resulted in the development of often simple but highly effective water conservation techniques. Greywater is regularly used for irrigating tree nurseries and in Burkina Faso stone lines on the surface of the soil help prevent soil erosion and trap available water.

AUSTRALIA

Although a vast continent, Australia has a population of 17.5 million only, yet its gasoline/petrol consumption (per capita) is the third-largest in the world (after the US and Canada).

Australia is the world's largest exporter of coal and the third-largest user of water. Figures from the Australian Bureau of Statistics reveal that every Australian generates 680kg (1500lb) of waste compared with the average 512kg (1130lb) per person in OECD countries and 1905 in the US. The annual per capita emission of greenhouse gases is 11 tonnes, compared to an OECD average of 6.1 tonnes and 10 tonnes in the US.

Landfill sites are becoming scarcer, but at present **incineration** only accounts for 1-2% of solid waste disposal. Interest in recycling is growing, but slowly – the cheap cost of landfill hasn't actively promoted resource conservation or reuse. However Sydney is facing a landfill crisis following the shelving of plans for a new site due to environmental pressure. Instead the State government is setting up trial recycling schemes involving colour-coded bins for newspapers, **aluminium** drinks cans, and **glass** in public places. In New South Wales there is an innovative rebate scheme, funded by a levy on unrecycled waste sent to landfill; in turn councils also get paid for each tonne of waste collected for recycling.

The federal government has set up a programme promoting Ecologically Sustainable Development (ESD) to allay national concerns over misleading environmental claims on product labels. Producers of recycled products achieved verification for their products in 1992; these included egg cartons, vegetable trays, a range of carry bags and a variety of insulating materials manufactured from telephone directories.

Following concern about groundwater and surface water pollution and prompted by recall programmes for certain chemicals, awareness about items that could be called household hazardous waste is becoming widespread. Already special collection facilities exist in five of the six territories and states, including kerbside collection for waste oil. More than 60% of all lead from vehicle **batteries** is returned to battery manufacturers for reuse.

Australia claims to be a world leader for a multinational fast food chain withdrawing foam plastic **packaging** and replacing it with paper wrappings. Although approximately one-third of Australia's paper is recycled, the main use is only low-grade packaging. The low cost of virgin **wood pulp** acts as a disincentive against a greater use of recycled paper. But the publishing trade aimed to be using up to 40% waste paper in newsprint by 1992. And the commercial reuse of shredded telephone directories into building insulation material proves that trial schemes can be economically successful.

The feasibility of recycling laminated **cartons** is under way. A pilot collection scheme in Sydney for fruit juice and milk cartons has proved very successful and has now been extended to Melbourne. Cartons are gathered through collection points provided by one of the supermarket chains, and in Tasmania a planned scheme involves drop-off points at certain service stations. Brisbane and Perth are now experimenting with kerbside carton collection.

In an attempt to achieve a better recovery rate, a deposit scheme of between five and ten cents on non-refillable drink containers (including **PET** bottles) has been successfully introduced. As a consequence of this participation rates have soared to between 85 and 95%. **Plastics** recovery mirrors the situation in other countries; recovery is still in its infancy at about 3%. A major survey to determine the importance of environmental issues on a variety of packaging products was cancelled in 1992 due to a lack of interest from manufacturers. Of the one million tonnes of plastic produced in 1989, 200,000 tonnes were used for packaging, and 70% for shortlife disposable products.

Thirty-six percent of used glass is collected, with a national target of 45% by 1995. But in metropolitan areas, kerbside collections already recover about 54% of glass, plus aluminium and PET bottles. Such collection schemes exist everywhere except South Australia, where legislation placing a deposit on containers was passed in 1975.

BRAZIL

This is a country of stark contrasts. It is the fifth-largest
country in the world, rich in many minerals and natural
resources, with three-quarters of the population living in the
towns and cities. Levels of poverty are high – the result of an
economic system that concentrates income (and land) rather
than distributing it. Shanty towns are found everywhere,
particularly in unwanted, unsafe locations – on hillsides,
riverbanks, roadsides, and on or near rubbish dumps.

Tin and **iron** ore mining has left its legacy on the
landscape and the lack of tough environmental standards has
led to certain transnational companies using parts of Brazil
for industrial processing work that is outlawed elsewhere.

The dumping of toxic waste is not unknown. In Sao Paulo
rivers have become open sewers.

On the edges of the cities whole communities are involved
in collecting, mending, and reusing other people's rubbish.

Recycling is more inventive than elsewhere; **plastic** milk
bags are made into tablecloths, flour sacks into hammocks,
tins into all sorts of containers, carriers, and lamps.

New initiatives to deal with the rising volumes of solid
waste are under way. Waste separators have formed
collectives for dealing with, and processing, wastes, and
there is renewed interest in composting.

CANADA
The country has a population of 26.5 million and is the world's second-largest energy user. Over 30 million tonnes of municipal **solid waste** is produced every year – more than one tonne for every individual. 10% is recycled, the rest goes to **landfill**. Further expansion of **incineration** was outlawed in Ontario late in 1992.

Canada contains 10% of the world's forests, much of it the irreplaceable boreal forest in British Columbia, already devastated to feed the growing demands of the **paper** industry. Paper in Canada is 60% cheaper than in Sweden, another major producer and 31% of the global supply of newsprint comes from Canada. Yet every year Canadians dump five million tonnes of waste paper in landfills, amounting to 35% of their solid waste. Pollution around pulp and processing mills fuels the vigorous "Reach for the Unbleached" environmental campaign. In an attempt to reuse more paper, thermal insulation materials from wood-based cellulose fibre are being developed – some have already received the seal of approval – the Canadian Eco-Logo – as part of the Environmental Choice eco-labelling programme.

By the end of the year 2000 Canada is planning to cut waste by 50%, according to its ambitious Green Plan. **Packaging** accounts for 30% of the waste stream, and is the largest single component; a National Packaging Protocol applying the four Rs – Reduce, Reuse, Recycle, and Reclaim – is being developed.

The newsprint industry is now recovering more than 50% of Ontario's newsprint. Ontario also collects over 40% of its **cardboard**, 33% of **glass**, 52% of plastic **PET**, and 52% of **wood**. Government funding has made 750,000 home composting units available, which will cut about 40% of household waste from collections. British Columbia has passed a bill requiring a minimum recycled content in goods, as well as life cycle analyses, waste audits, and packaging reduction plans. An expansion of the deposit scheme on drinks containers is planned.

The federal government in Canada is also committed to tackling waste in government-owned buildings; a waste reduction and recycling programme has been implemented. Practical measures include: staff having recycling boxes at their desks; **envelopes** being reused; instructions on the more efficient use of photocopiers, and reusable mugs sold, with discounted drinks for those that use them.

Opportunities for greater reuse of industrial waste is part of a national waste exchange programme.

Canada originally led the way in developing the "separation at source" concept using the "Blue Box" for kerbside collections. This scheme, started in the early 1980s, was made mandatory for communities of over 5000 people. Although the Blue Box scheme has been criticized for not placing enough emphasis on waste reduction, it has served as a role model for European countries. Another world first, a recycling litter bin was launched in Toronto in 1991 as a response to studies that revealed that 70% of litter was actually recyclable. The new bin has compartments for glass, **cans**, and **newspaper**, as well as litter.

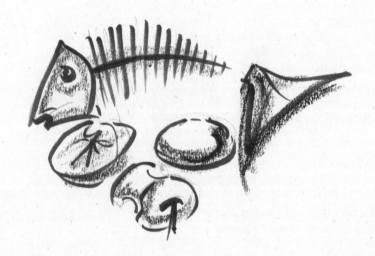

CHINA

China has one-fifth of the world's population but only 7% of its arable land; as a result the Chinese have, out of necessity, been conscious of reusing and recycling animal and human waste for agriculture, and they reclaim other materials that other countries would normally dismiss as waste. One traditional slogan is "all waste is treasure". Composting techniques were already in use over 4000 years ago, and the practice of applying nightsoil, or human sewage, to agricultural land is an ancient one. Shanghai, with its population of nine million, manages to produce a surplus of vegetables from the sewage-fed, agricultural "greenbelts" surrounding the city. Because garbage is also mixed with nightsoil for composting, separate collection programmes exist for residential and industrial wastes; knowing the source is vital for keeping hazardous wastes out of compost.

Plastic bags are precious, and once acquired are constantly reused. In rural areas the everyday task of carrying things still rely on traditional techniques of weaving reeds into baskets; burning these in the fields at the end of the day is a still-practised ritual. There are deposits on every **bottle** and **jar** – the **glass** can be worth more than its contents and everywhere there are active reuse and recovery programmes. In Shanghai one plant retrieved more than 20 million tonnes of waste metal, **paper**, cloth, plastics, and **rubber** between 1957 and 1982. Municipal purchasing and redemption centres exist where residents and salvagers are paid for the materials they bring in.

Once a world leader in the numbers of bicycles produced each year, great reliance is still placed on small-scale repair workshops for all types of items.

COMMONWEALTH OF INDEPENDENT STATES (CIS)
The former Soviet Union is one of the world's biggest steel
producers (the others are China, Japan, Germany, and the
US), but very little is recycled.

A legacy of polluted air, land, and water exists. The extent
of pollution is severe; Lake Baikal in Siberia, the oldest and
deepest lake in the world, is poisoned by heavy metals in the
effluent that runs into it. Scientists predict that even if
dumping stopped today, the lake would take several hundred
years to rejuvenate.

Most housing in the cities is in apartment buildings
requiring centralized collections and rubbish chutes. In
Moscow there is a vacuum system of removing household
wastes through special sewers, prior to **incineration**. Most
other cities **landfill** solid wastes, although composting is also
practised.

 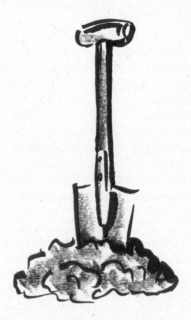

DENMARK

With a population of 5.1 million, Denmark has the best record in Europe for implementing European directives concerned with reuse or recycling of household waste. The Danish government has set a recycling target of 40-50% of household waste by the year 2000. In 1989, only 12% of waste ended up in **landfill**. **Incineration**, with energy recovery, is the favoured disposal method, accounting for over 60% of the country's wastes.

Disposable drinks **packaging** was banned in 1979 by the government; a decision upheld in the Court of Justice of the European Community on the grounds that the system contributes significantly to the protection of the environment. 400 million **bottles** are returned for refilling every year – 150 million for soft drinks and 250 million for beer; each bottle is returned about 32 times in its four-year life cycle and the crates are included within the system. Proposals for deposits on imported bottles have been made.

Legislation is also used to promote the recycling of **newspapers** and other **paper**, collected through paper banks and collection schemes operated by commercial companies. In 1990, 409,000 tonnes of waste paper were collected, 267,000 of those were recycled in Denmark. Writing paper and 100% recycled **envelopes** are widely promoted and used and many **cardboard** boxes are returned for reuse.

Separate collection of hazardous household materials is compulsory in Denmark. Arrangements are left to the local municipalities to organize, but most cities have both mobile and kerbside collections. **Paint** can be returned to paint retailers and as in many European countries, they have their own special collection bins. The use of **PVC plastic** is discouraged because of the pollution threat if burned.

Denmark pioneered a Green Waste scheme – encouraging householders to separate organic household waste for composting – as a means of reducing waste. By mid-1990 over 100,000 people were sorting their wastes into the two-bin system – red for dry and green for wet (organic) wastes.

EGYPT

As in many developing countries, reuse and recycling is
commonplace, with a strong informal network of salvagers,
repairers, restorers, and reprocessors. The Zabbaleen, the
recycling community of Cairo, have developed a highly
organized community of rubbish collection, not only from the
urban tips but also from the city streets and commercial
establishments. A major proportion of the city's waste is now
collected by the Zabbaleen and World Bank funding has
allowed them to acquire better handcarts for extending
their schemes. The job of sorting valuable materials –
tin, **plastic**, and **glass** from organic wastes falls largely
to the women. Organic wastes are fed to pigs.

Small metalworking workshops abound; waste motor **oil** is
used to melt **aluminium** scrap for cooking pots.

EUROPEAN COMMUNITY (EC)

Recycling practices throughout the EC countries are varied,
but one of the most controversial aspects in terms of
legislation has been **packaging**. The EC as a whole currently
produces about 50 million tonnes of packaging waste every
year, yet only recycles about 18%, or 9 million tonnes.

The highly debated, yet finally agreed, draft EC Packaging
and Waste Directive (1992) requires that within ten years of
its ratification 90% of all used packaging must be valourized;
that is reused, recycled, composted, regenerated, or
incinerated with energy recovery. There is an additional
requirement that 60% of each material must be recycled. It
sets no targets for reducing or stabilizing the amount of
waste produced and it is acknowledged that there will be
pressure to reduce these figures.

Another contentious issue has been the proposal to
introduce an EC-backed eco-labelling system – commenced
in June 1993. Some manufacturers in certain countries are
already saying that they will boycott the scheme as the
standards are too tough; others are saying that they are not
tough enough.

FINLAND

The population of Finland is approximately five million. Nationally, 19-20% of all municipal waste, including commercial and industrial waste, is recycled. Helsinki, the capital, has a good recycling rate of 27%, but overall 95% of the country's domestic waste goes to **landfill**.

The Finnish government has set a recycling target of 50% for municipal **solid waste** by the year 2000. They plan to achieve this by materials recovery (37%) and energy recovery (13%). Although the level of paper recycling is high, most of the waste paper goes into newsprint production, **cardboard**, and **envelopes**. Little is used for high-grade purposes such as office stationery.

For drinks **packaging** there is a trend toward the returnable **bottle**, a move encouraged by the introduction of a packaging tax and packaging deposits. To be exempt a producer or importer of soft drinks will have to use an approved collection and recycling system. Refilling is encouraged through deposits on **bottles**. **Bottle banks** recover 20% of **glass**.

Plastic recycling is still in its early stages. In Helsinki there is a kerbside collection scheme, with alternative drop-off facilities for about 3000 households, and in East Helsinki (100,000 inhabitants) there are bottle banks for **plastic** containers. Helsinki airport operates a collection programme for both plastic film wrapping from cargo, and a range of multi-materials. Elsewhere, trial composting schemes are under way.

FRANCE

Recent legislation indicates that environmental issues are starting to play a significant role in preventing unnecessary amounts of waste from being deposited in **landfills**. Action to tackle the escalating level of waste (303kg/668lb of household waste per capita) has led the French government to introduce a new programme of waste management with the goal of closing landfills within the next decade.

A system similar to Germany's Duales System has been started, but unlike that system, which places emphasis on reuse and recycling, the French Packaging Decree (in force since January 1, 1993) also leaves the option open for **incineration**. Responsibility for disposing of **packaging** lies with the manufacturers, importers, and retailers in conjunction with ECO-Emballage, set up by industry with government approval, to co-ordinate the collection and disposal of household waste. By January 1 1997, industry must meet the 75% collection and valorization target.

The **packaging** industry in France is now the country's eighth-biggest economic sector, representing 2% of France's GDP. The food industry uses two-thirds of the total amount of packaging consumed in France. Out of all the packaging materials used, **plastic** has experienced the biggest growth level (**glass** comes third on the scale, and metals fourth).

Currently packaging accounts for approximately 40% of the 26 million tonnes of household waste; 90% of liquid food packaging is not reclaimed – creating a much higher proportion of waste than the European average of 60%. Landfill accounts for about 35% of municipal solid waste disposal, with **incineration** rates of over 35%. In order to promote recycling and incineration with energy recovery, a landfill tax on household and non-toxic waste is proposed. There is an almost total ban on waste imports following the discovery of German domestic and packaging waste being dumped in France – some of which was contaminated.

GERMANY

The country's population is approximately 77 million. Much of the published material on Germany's recycling record is based on the former West Germany, one of the most world's most advanced nations for waste reduction and recycling programmes. This is now a time of great change for the whole country and, for the inhabitants of former East Germany, access to a much wider range of consumer goods means that the low volume of waste is predicted to rise sharply from the annual 150-180kg (330-397lb) per person. In West Germany the average waste per person is 380kg (837lb) a year, a total of 30-32 million tonnes.

The German eco-labelling scheme – the Blue Angel – was the first voluntary scheme in the world to denote products with a higher environmental compatibility than others with the same purpose. Although it has proved to have its limitations, many other countries have used it as a role model in developing their own. Overall, Germany continues to tighten its legislation on waste and **packaging**. The Avoidance of Waste (Packaging) Ordinance introduced in 1991 has caused widespread controversy within the packaging trade, both inside and outside the country. Under the Duales System, producers and retailers are obliged to accept packaging back for reuse or recycling, with the ultimate aim of recycling 90% by 1995. This has led to vast quantities of material being collected. Unfortunately the expansion of end markets has not kept pace with collection, so German manufacturers have been found to be shipping their collected waste abroad, causing problems with commodity markets in other countries.

In October 1992 Germany announced two proposals – one regulation would raise the amount of beverages packaged in refillable containers from the current target of 72% to 84%, and it would include milk, currently exempt from legislation. The other regulation concerns bringing containers of hazardous materials within Germany's take-back rules.

About 35% of Germany's waste is incinerated; up to 30 more incinerators are planned. Annual paper consumption in

West Germany is approximately 13 million tonnes; manufacturers already use up to 60% waste paper content in papermaking processes. Over 39% of **glass** and 45% of **steel** cans (used more than **aluminium**) are recycled and potentially hazardous items such as **batteries** are collected separately. Most chemists take back unused medicines, and often small batteries, too. Many towns have facilities for household hazardous waste, including **paint** and aerosols. Munich and Frankfurt have specialized mobile collection vehicles. Organic waste from kitchens and gardens is collected through various Green Bin systems for centralized composting. **Plastic** packaging with the Green Dot is collected through the Duales System.

As a result of threat of government action to tackle vehicle waste, Germany has become a world leader in investigating the recovery and reuse of materials used in vehicle manufacture. Six dismantling plants are in operation, and others are planned for the rest of Europe. It was the first country to provide collection facilities on the forecourts of service (petrol) stations for DIY mechanics to deposit **oil** and other potentially polluting fluids from **cars**.

Under a new decree (not yet law) from 1997 all batteries in France will have to be collected and recycled. Responsibility for this lies with manufacturers and importers: a tax on batteries will be used to finance the project, including the construction of a battery recycling plant.

INDIA

In 1991 India's total population was 846 million people, with approximately 250 million living in the urban areas. Although the practice of reuse and recycling is widespread throughout the nation, there is still about one thousand tonnes of **solid waste** – mainly wet organic matter – which needs disposal each day. To reduce the amount that has to be dumped and to cut the transport costs involved in hauling material to incinerators or biogas plants, innovative composting techniques, including the use of worms (**vermiculture**) are under investigation. Although such techniques produce a high-quality compost, researchers in Bombay acknowledge that the lure of western technology acts as a powerful disincentive to adopt such appropriate technologies.

On the world scale, India is becoming a major supplier of **iron** and **steel**, and nationwide there is a host of small-scale industries reusing materials, including small workshops that produce **tools**, water carriers, and household utensils from scrap. Scissor-making from scrap steel and iron is an example of a traditional practice that is often carried on by the next generation. Each kilo (2lb) of scrap produces about three pairs of scissors, but the preparation and grinding work is arduous and often dangerous. Small-scale repair workshops are also found everywhere; for a nation that produces 8% of the world's total number of bicycles, engineering spare parts and undertaking repair is an everyday practice.

Like so many other cities in developing countries, a strong informal recycling infrastructure exists. Salvaging other people's waste for recycling is a way of life for the people who live on and off the rubbish dumps. In Dhapa, East Calcutta, the city's waste dump supports thousands of people who eke out a living by sifting through the piles of rubbish for **paper**, **glass**, **textiles**, **tin**, **rubber**, cork, and other materials they can sell to traders for recycling. Some even grow vegetables, which are then sold in the city, on the piles of rotting humus. Initiatives started up locally to help improve the health and welfare of the rubbish pickers and their families are being supported by Oxfam.

Even the lowest grades of rag waste (chindi) from textile mills provide a source of income for rag pickers, who are mostly women. The chindi is either sold on to traders or the women working in organized collectives making and selling quilts. In Bangladesh, women recycle old sari cloth into quilts and cushion covers. Shoes are frequently made from cut-up car **tyres**.

Aquaculture technologies using waste water and foodstuffs yield about eight tonnes of fish per hectare per year in India; in Calcutta (with its population of 13 million) sewage is added to enrich the water, providing 20,000kg (44,092lb) of fish a day for sale. Certain species, such as Tilapia, convert low-grade organic wastes into a high-class protein, and they thrive in mildly polluted waters. Sewage is also reused in small-scale projects, composting refuse and **nightsoil**, while biogas plants convert organic wastes into fuel for normal domestic use.

Effective solid waste management schemes, involving the local community using closed containers for their waste rather than dumping it in the streets, are now being phased in to prevent pollution of rivers, such as the Ganga, through uncontrolled dumping and untreated water. To date the schemes have been successful.

ITALY

With 57.5 million inhabitants and a rising tide of waste, Italy
is an example of a European country trying to control,
through legislation, the types of packaging in use. Since
January 1990 separate collections have existed for a range of
materials and recycling targets have been set. By the end of
1992, it was expected that 50% of **glass** and metals, and 40% of
plastics, as well as multi-material **packaging**, would have to
be collected for recycling. There is a special tax – 10%
surcharge – on plastic packaging. **Incineration** with energy
recovery is allowed for 20% of the mixed packaging and
plastic waste; but if materials do not meet the recycling
targets by 1993, a tax will be introduced.

PVC and **PET** are collected by Blue Bottle Eaters –
collection banks sited in supermarket car parks. There is a
mandatory National Consortium for the Recycling of Plastic
Liquid Containers, funded by the 10% levy on plastic
containers. They are obliged to recycle 40% of the plastics
used in containers in Italy. Additionally, there are lots of
other plastic recovery programmes, including ones for
containers previously used for car products such as anti-
freeze and lubricant oil – these are remanufactured into new
containers. Plastic film has been recovered from municipal
solid waste since 1975; it is converted into all kinds of
moulded plastic goods.

At present over 40% of glass and 29% of **aluminium** cans
are recycled. The city of Rome has recycled a variety of
materials since 1964. In 1984 the World Bank estimated the
annual benefits to include: saving over 400,000 trees;
improving soil quality through the application of organic soil
additives to 60,000 acres of agricultural land, and saving over
30,000 tonnes of fuel.

Batteries and medical waste are collected separately for
safe disposal. Italy is a world leader in developing
composting technologies for organic waste, including the use
of sewage sludge.

JAPAN

With a population of over 123 million people crammed into such a small area (only the size of California) and with a lack of agricultural land, Japan has had to develop effective new programmes to tackle waste. The existing dumps are rapidly filling and new sites are difficult to find. Rubbish "islands" have been created in Tokyo Bay in an attempt to alleviate the situation. Overpackaging is the norm, but now Japan has adopted a "waste not, want not" policy to decrease its reliance on imported goods, which total 99% of its **oil**, 92% of its iron, and 100% of its copper. Making the most efficient use of energy and materials is a policy that has allowed Japan to sell goods much cheaper than competing nations. It already has a reputation as one of the developed world's most energy-efficient countries. Although Japan produces 15% of the world's wealth, using 5% of its energy, per capita emissions of greenhouse gases are less than half of America's. New measures to tackle energy consumption from its continuing programme of growth were outlined in a radical document "Proposals for a New Earth", 1993. Carbon taxes were dismissed in favour of tax incentives for industry, commerce, and households.

Japan's first recycling law, introduced in 1991, encourages manufacturers to increase their use of recycled materials; non-complying companies are fined. However **plastics** are not covered by this legislation, making waste-reduction schemes vital. In 1989 Tokyo and Osaka produced 50,000 tonnes of waste **paper** and 25,000 tonnes of **plastic** waste every day. The Earth-Works Group in Berkeley, California, estimates that from 100,000 tonnes of typical Japanese rubbish comes enough wood pulp to make a roll of toilet paper that would wrap around the world ten times.

After the US, Japan is the second-biggest producer of rubbish in the world, yet its recycling rate is reported to be 50%. Critics doubt the validity of this figure since accurate recycling data is not kept. **Incineration** with energy recovery accounts for 75% of waste disposal. In terms of household hazardous waste, there is no formal recognition, but substances such as **mercury** and used engine **oil** are being targeted for collections and around half the municipalities collect **batteries**, fluorescent tubes, thermometers, and mirrors. Several cities have pipeline collections of used oil, which is sold for re-refining.

Japan does have a problem with toxic waste; there is incomplete monitoring data and substances such as **cadmium** and **lead** are not classified as hazardous. But what legislation does exist is generally much stricter than other industrialized nations – policies are based on strict liability – the polluter pays. However Japan also has a bad reputation for "exporting" its most toxic manufacturing processes, as well as deforestation practices, to the coast of south-east Asia.

The country has its own eco-labelling scheme – the Eco Mark, which is unusual in that it extends to covering the activities of local authorities setting up waste reduction and recycling programmes.

MEXICO

Mexico City, with its population of 15 million people and 3.5 million vehicles, has gained world renown for being one of the most polluted cities on Earth. The air pollution is now a direct threat to health. Down on the US-Mexico border lies another problem. The border industrialization programme and the little control exercised over companies' activities has encouraged multinationals to site their dirty industries and assembly plants for the US market within Mexico. The foreign exchange earned is second only to Mexico's oil and gas exports, but the visible water pollution and the production of 20 tonnes of hazardous waste per year is a high price to pay. And it is the poor who suffer.

Within Mexico City there are about 10,000 urban poor, who search the rubbish dumps, such as Santa Fe, for food to eat and items to sell, but at what price to their health? Like other cities, the informal recycling structure is based in the shanty town communities. Systems have evolved where municipal rubbish collectors will sell their load to the highest bidder, so at the main dump site in Mexico City agents for various groups of scavengers compete against each other to get the truck to dump in their area.

Pressure from environmental groups is leading to new developments in Mexico. Following the 1992 Earth Summit in Rio de Janeiro, the President is reported to be viewing environmental action as the most cost-effective action, and questions concerning the priority issues that need tackling are being asked. At the local level grassroots groups in towns are organizing river clean-ups. According to one spokesperson they are trying to rationalize the use of resources, with the collaboration of regional authorities. The proportion of food waste is high, due partly to a lack of **packaging**, making municipal composting programmes a more viable option.

NETHERLANDS

With a population of 14.7 million, the Netherlands is known throughout the world as a country with high-technology industry, intensive agriculture and livestock farming, and one of the densest motorway networks, with a high car use per head of population. The combination of these activities make it, by its own admission, one of the most heavily polluted countries in Europe.

Waste is a national problem – not only the large quantities of visible waste but also the invisible waste, particularly of energy within industry and agriculture. Reuse and recycling is crucial to a country that does not have enough space for waste dumping. A recent study found that every Dutch person produces as much waste as a small business in the developing world. However the Dutch government's National Environmental Policy Plan, 1989, and a recent update, illustrates just how far governments can take a lead in applying principles of sustainable development to a whole country. Issues being tackled include the continuing export of toxic chemical wastes; controls over the environmental impact – "cradle to grave" assessment – of products, and additional energy conservation measures.

Recycling rates for domestic waste are high and in the battle to minimize waste, the Netherlands ranks with Germany as European leader in environmental affairs. For example, tough new policies designed to tackle **packaging** waste were announced in June 1991. The Dutch government, in consultation with industry, agreed measures to reduce the volume of packaging waste from 2.7 million tonnes to 1.9 million tonnes by the end of the century. By the year 2000, there must be a 10% reduction of packaging by weight and 60% of packaging materials must be capable of being reused or recycled.

There is to be a ban on **landfill**; currently 40% of waste is landfilled and over 25% incinerated. The new proposals allow an **incineration** rate of up to 40%, but the Dutch Environment Ministry wants to keep amounts as low as possible and energy recovery must be part of the incineration process. The Dutch government has warned the EC that the Netherlands will not accept the EC Packaging and Packaging Waste Directive if it is not as tough as the country's existing recycling regime.

The Netherlands is renowned for its large number of **bottle banks** per head of population. On average a single site serves fewer than 1500 people; as a result the **glass** reclamation rate is over 54%. Dutch research demonstrates that the number of bottle banks is very important – people are generally unwilling, nor is it environmentally desirable, to travel far to deposit **bottles**. Drinks are also sold in refillable, returnable plastic **PET** bottles. **Steel** can recovery is about 45%. Other items collected for reprocessing include credit cards, used drink crates, clothes hangers, and **bottle tops**.

Getting householders to separate organic food wastes for composting programmes is being tried in some areas, as well as the composting of fruit and vegetable waste from street markets. Some cities have set high targets for organics; in Arnhem the city is already collecting 85% of organic materials in one-sixth of the city, plus 45% of **glass** (the target is 90%) and 33% of **paper**.

For other materials – household hazardous chemicals, **batteries**, **paint**, obsolete **electrical equipment**, computers, and **white goods**, Arnhem, in conjuction with other cities, is developing collections to salvage reusable materials or parts for resale or remanufacture. The rest goes for safe disposal.

Getting people to recycle yet more waste is being actively pursued by action on a government report, which suggested the use of corner stores as mini-recycling centres. The idea is that people drop off materials en route to work or shopping; in future these sites could become full recycling centres, creating new "work from waste" opportunities.

PHILIPPINES

Among the slums and urban deprivation of Metro-Manila
(population 8 million) exist 5000 scavengers who depend on
other people's waste for their own survival. The infamous
open-air dump site known as Smokey Mountain is picked
over daily by the low-income urban poor scavenging for
resaleable scraps. The numbers allowed on to the main dump
site are limited. Every rubbish-picker can expertly identify all
the different types of **plastic**, and knows the local price of
various salvaged metals. Discarded tin **cans**, broken
cardboard, old **car** parts all have a value. In an attempt to
lessen the stigma of salvaging, recycling programmes have
been set up to get citizens to perceive wastes as recyclable
materials. Plastic bags are sold to local market traders, or
reprocessed into "raffia", animal bones are sold for **adhesive**
making, and **paper** and magazines are either resold for
wrappings, or sold to mills for remanufacture.

The number of informal junk shops and second-hand
centres has meant that many of the municipal redemption
centres have had to close.

Re-use is becoming a commonly accepted idea. In a
programme co-ordinated by the Metro-Manila Council of
Women Balikatan Movement (a non-governmental
organization) dry household wastes are collected and
returned to factories for re-manufacturing. The programme
has existed for the best part of a decade. Householders are
encouraged to keep separate containers in the kitchen for
dry and wet wastes. These are collected on an organized
basis by traditional junkstore owners, who pay for the dry
wastes. The organizing Council supplies the collectors with
special carts and boats that service the rivers.

Throughout the Philippines there is a mixture of high-
technology reclamation programmes, as well as labour-
intensive, small-scale technologies reusing and composting
agricultural wastes, **oil**, **plastics**, metals and other items.
Vermiculture is promoted as a way of reducing the volume
of waste by 50% – the worm castings are reused within city
parks and on farms.

POLAND

With many materials in short supply, informal reuse has always taken place, but now more organized recycling programmes are under way. The legacy of pollution from inappropriate waste management has left pollution levels higher than they should be.

In Katowice a source separation scheme for household wastes is under way, using different-coloured boxes for **paper/cardboard**, **organic waste**, **glass**, and **cans**. The amount of food and organic materials in the waste is high so composting is practised. An energy-from-waste scheme, providing fuel for electricity production and district heating, is to be built. And Poland encounters similar problems to other countries in the lack of public information and awareness hampering further developments.

SPAIN

Compared to other European countries, Spain's environmental movement is not well developed and therefore many opportunities are perceived to exist in terms of greater resource conservation. In the 1980s the rate of increase in waste production in Spain was one of the highest within the OECD countries: a 50% increase. The current situation in Spain has been described as a "time of transition". In 1991 27% of **glass** was collected for recycling and there is increasing use of **plastic** in Spain. This, in turn, leads to disposal problems.

In some parts of the Andalusian region of southern Spain it is common to see nothing but a sea of plastic sheeting – the region is famous for its intensive crop-growing. The result is that more than 25,000 tonnes of agricultural plastic film is generated each year. The scale of the problem has led to new initiatives in Madrid, Tarragona, and Pamplona for collection and reprocessing. A plastics recycling plant is planned for Seville; research into new technologies will be conducted by a new foundation set up by the Spanish plastics industry, including well-known multinational companies.

SWEDEN

With a population of 8.3 million, Sweden is one of the most environmentally aware and energy-efficient countries in the world. It manufactures and exports high-quality electrical appliances and **white goods** with reduced CFC content, and has a system of refundable deposits on items, including **cars**, to encourage responsible disposal or return for scrap. Sweden, with its commercial forestry plantations, has led the world market in unbleached **paper** products, although it still produces chlorine-bleached pulp for export. Organochlorines in the effluent from Swedish pulp mills have caused severe ecological damage in the Baltic Sea – the area is now known locally as the "dead sea".

On the recycling front, an eco-labelling scheme is being introduced and by 1994, Sweden aims to be source-separating domestic waste. Household hazardous waste schemes exist for items such as **batteries**. The country generally has a high collection rate for materials, for example 82% of **aluminium cans** are available for recycling.

A report from the Swedish government recommends that by the year 2000 recycling rates should be: paper **packaging** 60%; **glass** 60-70% ; **aluminium** 60-80%; tinplate 40-60%, and **plastic** 30-40%. A tax on packaging would go to finance collection systems by producers and retailers, and all consumers should be separating waste. The forestry and paper industries disagree with government estimates on how much paper could be recycled and they want waste in rural areas to be incinerated to cut transport costs. Trial plastic collection schemes are starting. The country pioneered the waterless, compost toilet.

SWITZERLAND

Proving that retailers can take the lead and make a difference to recycling trends, Switzerland's largest distributer and retailer of food and household products (Migros) has introduced many environmental practices, including a "design for recycling" initiative, through its stores. The giant co-operative society has over 500 retail outlets, which strive to cut down **packaging** waste. Besides the self-service bulk dispensers for selling soap, detergents, and cosmetics, no-bleach detergent is sold in biodegradable paper sacks, and toothpaste and other products are sold in tubes without the outer **cardboard** packaging. Wherever possible products contain a percentage of recycled material, and old packaging is reused – in 1991 67% of all wrappers were recycled. The company has developed a computer programme that highlights the most ecologically sustaining form of packaging or product. As a result the switch from cardboard boxes to reusable **plastic** crates saves 60,000 tonnes of cardboard a year. In 1989 600,000 tonnes of Switzerland's rubbish was trucked to sites for burning – 10% was packaging.

Plastic **PET** bottles have been collected since 1991 through a scheme established by the **glass** industry and similar pilot schemes for **PVC** were proving to be successful by the end of 1991 – with a high recovery rate of 45%. A pilot scheme for returnable, refillable PET drinks bottles proved such a success that other countries, including Germany and the Netherlands, are now using them. **Bottles** are laser-marked when refilled and after 26 trips they are sent for recycling. Laminated cards, including credit cards and telephone cards are collected for recycling. In 1992 it was predicted that 500 tonnes would be collected.

In Zurich a city-wide composting programme, aimed at apartment dwellers, was in existence by the middle of 1991.

A public information programme advises residents on how to choose the best site for backyard composting and gives instructions on how to compost.

TURKEY

Returnable **glass bottles** and refilling operations remain common throughout Turkey, but gradually non-returnable glass containers are being introduced. However, according to Europe-wide statistics for the amount of glass collected through **bottle banks**, Turkey actually recycles more glass than the UK.

Metalwork repair and salvage operations exist and reuse of materials is practiced. Not every town or village has an organized rubbish collection, so informal systems exist, with salvagers who collect door-to-door using handcarts. They sell the materials on to collectors, who transport wastes to merchants with sorting yards.

UK

With a population of 56 million, the UK does not have an impressive recycling record compared with many of its European neighbours. Over 20 million tonnes of domestic solid waste is produced every year. The government's own estimates reveal that up to 50-60% (by weight) consists of potentially recyclable materials, yet the recycling rate is only 5 to 6% of household waste. There are no figures or targets available for the larger waste streams, which include agricultural waste, construction and demolition debris.

The majority of domestic waste is landfilled, with **incineration** only accounting for about 8%. A tough challenge lies ahead if the UK is to meet the target set by the government in its 1990 White Paper to recycle at least 25% of household waste by the end of the century. Unlike the US and many European countries the UK relies solely on the voluntary approach, rather than legislation, to promote recycling. Until now too little attention has been given to waste minimization programmes. Tighter controls over the operation of **landfill** sites and a new licensing process for all waste disposal is now in force and the government hopes that these measures will divert more material for recycling.

The most established collection methods are the drop-off sites such as **bottle banks**. First established in 1977 they now provide over 300,000 tonnes of **glass** for recycling each year. However the number of bottle banks per head of population is relatively low – only one for every 12,000 people. Research indicates that up to 40% of glass in household waste could be recovered, but only if there were more bottle banks. This would mean providing six times as many banks – one for every 2000 people. Other materials collected in this way include drinks **cans** – both **steel** and **aluminium**, steel food cans through "Save-a-Can", and in some areas paper, **plastic** bottles, and textiles.

Schemes for returning and refilling bottles are now largely confined to the dairy industry (milk bottles) and some breweries. Of the 6 billion glass containers used every year in the UK, 5 billion end up in the dustbin/garbage bin.

Community recycling schemes operated by not-for-profit groups have been hard-hit by fluctuating prices for waste paper and many no longer collect **newspaper**. Some schemes have developed into successful small businesses such as the Leeds-based "Save Waste and Prosper" and Milton Keynes' CROP. Success depends very much on developing a partnership approach with the local authority and reclamation industry.

The number of schemes operating on a kerbside-collection basis is growing, but most are still on trial. The first established scheme in Sheffield was, by January 1992, serving nearly 8000 households, and the range of materials collected had extended from just glass, paper, plastics, and cans to cover textiles and aluminium foil as well.

Since then many local authorities have started experimenting with composting schemes to reduce the proportion of waste requiring disposal. Many of the trial projects involve issuing householders with composting bins, and even worm composting (**vermiculture**) kits.

As this book goes to press, it is clear that new measures are being discussed by Government to find a workable regulatory system to tackle the diversion of used packaging from landfill.

USA

According to the Media Foundation, the US has 8% of the world's population, consumes one-third of the world's resources, and produces almost half of the world's non-organic rubbish. Estimates suggest that an average US household discards 1800 **plastic** items, 13,000 individual **paper** items, 500 **aluminium cans**, and 500 **glass** bottles every year. The US produces about half a tonne of rubbish per person per year. Calculated over a lifetime an individual will throw away 600 times their own weight.

A 1992 study by the Environmental Protection Agency (EPA) shows that although the total amount of municipal **solid waste** (MSW) had increased to 195 tonnes by 1990, up from 179 tonnes in 1988, recycling was beginning to have a significant impact on the solid waste stream. The total amount of MSW recycled or composted grew to 33.4 million tonnes in 1990 – an increase of 42% from 1988. By 1990 17.1% of municipal solid waste was being recycled. Garden/backyard wast composting sites increased by 56% to over 2000 operating schemes in 1990. By 1995 the EPA predict that 20 to 30% of municipal solid waste will be recycled or composted, and 25 to 35% by 2000.

The majority of rubbish goes into **landfill** – in 1990 this totalled 130 million tonnes of material. Nationally there are 6600 sites, but 10 states have less than 5 years' landfill capacity left. Spiralling disposal costs are adding to the crisis. On current projections the EPA predicts that less than half of municipal solid waste will be landfilled by the year 2000. Approximately 10% of rubbish is incinerated, but the number of plants operating without energy-recovery programmes has dropped substantially as a result of tighter air pollution regulations. Instead many communities are opting for better materials' recovery and recycling facilities. These include: regular kerbside pick-ups of recyclables (2711 schemes in 1990); drop-off sites in supermarket car parks and similar convenient locations, and recycling undertaken in buy-back centres run by private operators or not-for-profit organizations, who pay for the quantities of drinks cans or bottles brought in.

A 1992 survey of the 50 largest US cities reveals that 47 have either an established kerbside recycling programme or have a pilot project running. Community recycling schemes are plentiful and cities such as Minneapolis have programmes whereby private haulers or community groups are paid a "diversion" fee for every tonne of rubbish that does not go to landfill.

Although individual states have passed legislation controlling waste or requiring maximum reuse and recycling of specific materials, the amount of municipal waste is still expected to rise from 180 million tonnes a year to more than 250 million by the year 2010. It is extremely difficult to make statements about the extent of recycling because of the sheer size of the US, and also because legislation and regulations vary so much from state to state, and even regionally. But overall the Environmental Protection Agency predicts that up to 25% of municipal solid waste could be recoverable by 1995.

After investment in high-tech solutions to manage as much rubbish as possible, there is now renewed emphasis on waste reduction and recycling. Finding more markets for recycled goods is critical for the economic success of recycling and because so many US programmes mandate the collection of materials. Critics of recycling are only too eager to point to examples of stockpiles of recyclable materials which eventually end up in landfill, **incineration**, or are shipped half way around the world for disposal. In an attempt to stimulate positive procurement policies, the EPA issues guidelines covering items such as retread **tyres** and building insulation materials. New guidelines expect to cover construction materials, yard waste compost, and asphalt paving. Commercial examples of "closing the recycling loop" include high-grade recycled office and computer **paper**, recycled **plastic bottles**, **aluminium cans**, road signs, and fencing from post-consumer waste plastic, **carpet** fibres from **PET**, a synthetic construction "wood" from compressed drinks **cartons**, and crushed **glass** processed into a road surfacing material or used to make insulation boards.

The US is responsible for many pioneering initiatives. According to the well-respected Worldwatch Institute more people are employed in the recycling industry than in the metal mining industry. The world's first Bottle Bill was passed by Oregon as long ago as the 1970s. Leglislation is used to achieve enhanced rates of recycling; certain items such as garden/backyard waste are either banned from landfill, as in Seattle, or their use is totally prohibited (for example **polystyrene** packaging in parts of California). Putting a money-back deposit on containers is a favoured option – reducing the solid waste stream by 5%. However savings of 35% are possible through kerbside collection schemes, which are becoming widespread throughout the US. Attention is also being given to developing recycling and composting programmes for apartment dwellers.

Garden/backyard and community composting programmes are springing up throughout the nation as a response to the ban on garden/backyard waste in household rubbish. EPA findings suggest that by 1990 12% of garden/backyard waste was being composted compared with a "negligible" amount in 1988.

Seattle is the national leader in composting garden/backyard waste. Compost is sold back to city residents, public works departments, landscapers, and construction companies. A pioneering garden/backyard composting project also encourages householders to compost by issuing free compost bins, as well as running a full programme of training workshops, open days, and a telephone advice line. Information on making a variety of compost bins from low-cost or recycled materials is freely available as well as encouragement to try vermiculture. Currently about 20-25% of Seattle's single-family households compost their own garden/backyard wastes and Seattle has the highest number of worm bins per capita of any city in the country.

In 1991 industry refilled or recycled 31% of glass. Achieving more plastics recycling is a national goal; currently polythene and PET are the most widely collected plastics, with 36 states now having passed legislation requiring containers to carry the numbered coding system developed by the Society of the Plastics Industry.

Remaining competitive in the marketplace means that many manufacturers have had to adopt environmentally responsible processes or products. A notable example is **packaging**. Guidelines on what constitutes an environmentally sensitive product are appearing. For example, advice published by the Coalition of Northeastern Governors (CONEG) states in order of preference: no packaging; minimal packaging; and lastly recyclable packaging or materials made with a recycled content. The New York-based Public Interest Research Group (PIRG) issues a pamphlet for customers "Plagued by Packaging", which recommends avoiding single-use, disposable items, or non-recyclable packaging, and toxic packaging.

Although recyclability and reusability are widely used within the US as criteria for legislation banning environmentally "unfriendly" materials, the EPA is taking action to limit the confusing number of definitions. For example, in Massachusetts a recyclable package is defined as one made from material that will have achieved a recycling rate of at least 35% by the year 2000 (and 50% after that), while Oregon considers a product recyclable if it is included in an effective recycling programme. "Effective recycling" is taken to mean a 15% rate by 1993 and 60% by 2002. In an attempt to break through such confusion, Rhode Island set an important precedent which came into force at the end of 1991. To be considered "reusable" a package has to be capable of being reused or refilled a minimum of five times for its original purpose. The term "recyclable" is only permitted if it has achieved a 50% recycling rate, or is specially listed as a recyclable material. Using the wording "recycled" or "recycled content" is only permitted if information is provided on the percentage of material that is pre-consumer or post-consumer waste.

The US currently has two eco-labelling schemes; the Green Cross, launched in 1990, and the Green Seal, an initiative from the Earth Day organizer Randy Hayes.

ISSUES

Our whole way of life in the developed world, with its elaborate material trappings, needs careful re-examination. Clothes and cars are two major consumables that we are inclined buy new before the old has been thoroughly worn out. The repercussions are far-reaching.

Fashion pollution

Every year the catwalks of the major fashion houses vibrate with the latest creations of fabrics, accessories, and whims of the multi-million fashion industry. The clothes may be impractical and faddy, but the high street stores swiftly copy and adapt the designs to meet customer demand. The industry is built on dreams, but behind the scenes, and often across the oceans, lies the harsh reality of environmental and social impact.

Producing textiles from raw materials is energy-intensive and polluting. When countries impose tighter standards companies are forced to alter their practices or shut down. Some move to places where standards are laxer; the developing world is a sitting target. Most of the waste, some containing potentially highly toxic chemicals, results from de-sizing and scouring processes. The bleaching and colouring process adds to the pollution load and is often all too visible in the local environment, often posing a threat if the water or land used for growing crops, fish farming, bathing, or drinking becomes contaminated.

Reach for the unbleached

As a response to increasing consumer awareness about environmental issues, unbleached cottons are promoted by sections of the fashion industry and a growing breed of designers are creatively incorporating waste and recycled materials into their clothes. But these are not yet mainstream

Second-hand rose

The current anti-fashion "grunge" look has sent reverberations through the fashion industry as it struggles to imitate the deliberate "dressed-down", second-hand look. The industry will continue to thrive, fuelled by those who have the money to spend, but perhaps this latest backlash heralds a new era where second-hand clothing will lose its second-best image.

Car culture

The car has become a precious status symbol - an object which, the advertising industry would lead us to believe, mirrors our personality, our desires, and our social aspirations. The messages of freedom, sensuality, and power are portrayed through extravagant advertising. No price is too high if it sells more cars. The car reigns supreme on our streets and more roads are built to accommodate yet more. Roads slash through environmentally priceless landscapes, and as pollution levels rise, technological fixes become only short-term measures. The dominance of the car remains undisputed.

Mobility at a price

The advertising industry glosses over the stark reality of our dependence: the smog in our skies, the lead in our blood, the acid rain-ravaged trees, the death in our streets, and the gridlock in our cities. Market analysts for the motor industry estimate that approximately 1.3 billion new vehicles will be produced in the 20-year period between 1991 and 2010. The greatest market is predicted to be in south-east Asia, but the aggressive advertising pressure in the developed nations will increase sales everywhere.

Car recyclability

The car is a massive user of resources, so advertisements now promote the recyclability of cars. Manufacturers jump on the bandwagon by demonstrating their environmental conscience - certain vehicle parts are now fabricated from materials that would have been landfilled. The era of the 100% recyclable car is almost with us. But a major problem remains with the number of mixed materials used in the manufacturing process. Identifying recyclables and disassembling them is costly and recovery is often limited. Scrapyards and dumps remain a testimony to the fact that most cars still end their short lives rusting away.

ISSUES

Other people's waste provides a vital resource the world over. In the developed countries there is good money to be made re-utilizing industrial waste, while on a smaller scale waste exchange schemes provide a direct reuse and potential recycling of discards, and community scrapstores reuse unwanted items. In the developing world highly organized scavengers live off dumps and landfills and make their homes there, too.

Alley entrepreneurs

In industrialized countries where recycling programmes actively encourage collections and where there is separation of recyclables from household waste, "alley entrepreneurs" can usually be found. It is common for the contents of kerbside boxes to disappear the night before pick-up. The problem is particularly rife in California, where the state-wide redemption programme has driven the buy-back price for aluminium to artificially high levels. In San Francisco the agency that runs the country's most comprehensive kerbside programme estimates that it loses about 25% of the contents of kerbside boxes - $10,000 worth of bottles and cans to "poachers" every week.

Unofficial recyclers

In Jakarta, Indonesia, officials actively encourage small-scale independent rubbish collectors, since waste disposal is one of the city's biggest problems. With 8 million inhabitants and waste dumps everywhere, the city would quickly become uninhabitable without these unofficial recyclers. Handcarts made from scrap wood and bicycle wheels are a common method of transporting pickings.

Garbage farming

In Calcutta, at the city's main dumping site, plots of matured land are leased out for vegetable farming - a highly productive activity due to the rich mixture of organic materials: vegetable waste, dung, sewage sludge, ash, and bones.

All over the world festivals and feasts are inherently linked with creating unnecessary waste; somehow the act of wasting itself has become an important part of celebration. But there is now a growing movement to counter this.

Christmas trees

Over 15 million trees every year in the UK end their growing days at Christmas - although there is a welcome trend toward chipping and shredding for mulch or composting. Many people prefer to buy artificial trees and reuse them every year - the cost is roughly equivalent to five real trees. Buying a living tree with roots is another option, but there is no guarantee of the tree's survival. Trees do need care.

Celebrate without wasting

Consumption - or overconsumption - at feasts and festivals can be a real eye-opener in terms of the amount of rubbish that is thrown away. It is not just the obvious wrappings and extra packaging but also the excess food, extra bottles, novelty items, and decorations. The end of the year festivities, whether religious or pagan, usually mark a period of renewal and rebirth. Perhaps it should also be a time to think of ways of celebrating without wasting. In Bali richly decorated food offerings are left for the gods, but only the "essence" is actually given to them. The donors take the food home to eat later and offerings to evil spirits are left to be eaten by village scavengers and dogs. Everyone enjoys the celebration and little is wasted.

Ritual burning

Throughout the world ritual burning of ceremonial waste or gifts is a common practice. The chiefs of the Kwakiutl Indians of North America reputedly vied with each other to give presents, which were then burned. And in Papua New Guinea elaborately constructed masks, using feathers, leaves, bark, raffia, and cane are burned after use. The masks represent the spirits and powers of the forest - a placatory feast is offered to protect local people and their crops for another season.

The
RECYCLER'S

A
to
Z

*"The real work of planet-saving will
be small, humble, and humbling, and
(insofar as it involves love) pleasing
and rewarding. Its jobs will be too many
to count, too many to report, too many to
be publicly noticed or rewarded, too
small to make anyone rich and famous."*
Wendell Berry - poet, essayist, farmer

A

ADHESIVES AND GLUE
Facts
Repairing **wood**, **cork**, **plastics**, fabric, or **rubber** often demands an adhesive or glue. Traditionally these were made from animal bones or natural latex derived from the rubber tree. But today many modern adhesives are based on petrochemical solvents that are often toxic, and if misused (inhaled), are harmful to health.

Reuse
Avoid using solvent-based adhesives; instead buy water-based glues or latex adhesives, which do not contain toxic solvents. Always follow manufacturers' instructions carefully and keep adhesives away from naked flames – many are highly flammable.

For glueing **paper** or card, and children's projects such as papier mâché, solvent-based glues are not necessary. Make up a safe flour and water glue (see below).

Thrift project
How to make flour and water paste
• Add three mugs of water to one mug of flour, in a pan, and stir in gradually to form a smooth paste.
• Bring to the boil, simmer for a few moments, and leave to cool. Keep refrigerated.

AEROSOL CANS
Facts
Aerosol cans are made from a mixture of materials that are impossible to recycle, and you cannot refill them, making them an extremely wasteful form of **packaging**. The CFC hazard (see **Glossary**) is well known, thanks to strong environmental pressure on manufacturers to phase out the use of the ozone-destroying CFC propellent gases. However some of the substitutes may in time prove to be just as bad.

When aerosols first appeared on the market in the 1940s, they were hailed as a wonderful invention, with attempts even to sell whisky in an aerosol. By 1987, 800 million were being made every year in the UK – 80% containing CFCs. Although most are now CFC-free, a better alternative is a recyclable and refillable **plastic (PET)** dispenser pack, currently on trial in the UK. This could join the refillable pump-action spray in providing a safe alternative for most non-essential uses.

Thrift project
How to make a flower pot-pourri
- Stretch a piece of muslin over a frame (i.e. an old picture frame).
- Dry flowers in single layers, keeping types separate, in a warm, dry place out of the sun. Lavender, rose, carnation, chamomile, and heliotrope combine well.
- When crisp, put the flowers in jars with tight-fitting lids, keeping types separate. Over each layer (2.5 cm/1 in deep) sprinkle ½ tsp coarse salt and ½ tsp orris root powder. Screw on the lids and store in a dark place for three weeks.
- Tip into a bowl and add any spices. Stir together gently and add a few drops of perfumed oil.

Reuse

Avoid buying aerosols – even the ones labelled "ozone-friendly" – and consider whether you really need the product at all. Aerosol air fresheners contain limonene, the "lemon" smell used in many household products, and tests have shown this to be a possible animal carcinogen. Instead open windows and use natural substances such as essential oils, scented dried flowers, or bowls of pot-pourri (see **Thrift project**). Buy hair preparations in refillable, pump-action sprays, deodorants as roll-ons or sticks, and household waxes and polishes in tins. Do not dispose of aerosols on bonfires – they explode.

ALLOYS

Facts

Many metals in common use today, and on which modern lifestyles rely, are actually alloys – blends of two or more metals combined to give added strength or increased resistance to rust. **Steel** is one of these. Made primarily from **iron** and carbon it forms the backbone of many countries' economies. Other alloys include brass (**zinc** and **copper**), pewter (**tin** and **lead**), and stainless steel (iron, carbon, chromium). Electrical appliances, **building materials**, **kitchen utensils**, **jewellery**, metal **paints**, **tools**, and vehicles are all made of alloys.

Reuse

Don't throw unwanted items in the dustbin/garbage bin. Give working equipment to **charity stores** or **jumble sales** for resale, or **scrap merchants** – brass and steel are always in demand.

Recycle

Recycle discarded **packaging** – keep **aluminium** and steel cans apart if separate collection systems operate in your area. That way a higher price is obtained for pure aluminium, and the steel is still recycled.

See also Salvage, White Goods

ALUMINIUM
Facts
This is a light-weight, strong metal that doesn't rust. It has a very high scrap value and can be recycled repeatedly without losing quality. In the latter part of 1990, aluminium production in industrialized countries reached a record 39,650 tonnes a day. The raw material is bauxite ore found in Brazil (2800 million tonnes equivalent), Guinea (5600 mte), Jamaica (2000 mte), and India (1000 mte). Over three billion tonnes of the world's bauxite reserves are in developing countries. It takes four tonnes of bauxite to make three tonnes of alumina, the oxide of aluminium. When this is reduced to pure aluminium, the yield is one tonne. It is this reduction process that makes aluminium production so energy-intensive.

Globally 22 million tonnes of aluminium is used every year – approximately 2.5% for packaging. Yet the high value of scrap aluminium and its energy-intensive nature make it an inappropriate material for disposable **packaging**. Recycling more aluminium is crucial; its production is environmentally destructive. Mining bauxite ore leaves a polluting red mud; the United Nations Environment Programme (UNEP) has been forced to set guidelines for land restoration by the major aluminium producers. Recycling saves 95% of the energy originally used to convert bauxite ore into aluminium.

Over 60% of the world's aluminium supply is produced using hydro-electric power. While this energy source does not produce large quantities of greenhouse gases, it does require large areas of land to be flooded, often destroying indigenous peoples' homelands. Generally, hydroelectric schemes are much more energy-efficient than coal-fired plants; as a result the aluminium industry is a permanent customer for the baseload production of hydro power stations.

Producing aluminium requires 14 kilowatt hours of electricity for smelting each kilo of aluminium from alumina. A kilo of aluminium is equivalent to 50 drinks cans. Scrap aluminium in developing countries is never wasted, in Egypt it is remelted using waste **oil**, and made into **saucepans** and **kitchen utensils**.

Aluminium use: 1988

	US	Japan	W.Europe
		(million tonnes)	
Packaging	30	8	7
Building	21	27	15
Transport	21	27	19
Electrical	9	7	6
Consumer durables	8	1	4
Mechanical	—	4	5
Others (including export)	11	26	44

Source: Metallgesemschaft and USBM

Reuse
Aluminium is poisonous and a link has been found between it and Alzheimer's disease. So do not cook acidic foods such as rhubarb in aluminium pans – the acids can cause small quantities of the metal to dissolve out. Use stainless **steel** instead. Collect aluminium drinks cans, **kitchen utensils, window frames,** and vehicle parts for recycling or send them to scrapyards. **See also** Aluminium cans, Aluminium foil

---

ALUMINIUM CANS
Facts
Put an aluminium drinks can in a dustbin/garbage bin and you throw away the energy equivalent of half a can of gasoline fuel. Globally, 50% of aluminium cans are collected for recycling, so 50% are thrown away. It is estimated that the US throws away enough aluminium every three months to completely rebuild their commercial airfleet.

Four out of every five drink cans in the world are made entirely from aluminium. In the US over 90% are aluminium; in Europe only 50% are pure aluminium, the rest are **steel**, or mixtures of both metals. The largest recyclers are Sweden (85%); Canada (63%); Australia (63%) US (62%), and Japan (42%). The UK recycling rate rose to 16% in mid 1992. New reprocessing plants are coming on stream in the UK, US, and

France. Figures from the International Primary Aluminium Institute (1989) reveal that a recycling plant only costs about 10% of the price of a primary ore smelter and yields a metal with only 5% of the energy input – giving a 95% energy saving.

Using less aluminium in the first place is important, too. The industry is tackling this by designing cans with a thinner wall, making them lighter – a process known as "lightweighting". Ten years ago the average drinks cans weighed 57.5 g (2 oz), compared to today's 30 g (1.5 oz). Lightweighting is also the industry's response to the challenge from plastic packaging, which is often used as an aluminium substitute.

Reuse/Recycle

Think before you buy drinks in cans – could you opt for refillable **glass** instead? Getting more aluminium recycled depends on more collection schemes and better labelling on cans. Without this, it is difficult for the consumer to know whether the can is all-aluminium or a mixture of metals. At present labelling is useful but not foolproof – not all aluminium can manufacturers use the "alu" label.

Unlike steel, aluminium is not magnetic, making sorting easy. Buy a small inexpensive magnet (magnetic strips are sometimes given away with publicity information) and test the body of the can, not the top. Some cans are **steel** with only an aluminium top – these cannot be included in aluminium collections unless you use a can opener to separate the metals. Keep steel for separate collections. Rinse and squash cans to reduce the amount of space they take up in sacks or can banks; a small wall-mounted can crusher will do the job.

Aluminium fetches a much higher scrap price than steel and many community groups collect it to raise funds. Set up a workplace or school recycling scheme – encourage people by giving the profits to a favourite charity. Comalco, in Australia, operates a can recycling programme in schools, offering prizes and money for cans returned. Both cans and clean foil may be cashed at Comalco's collection centres; since 1985 almost 10 million cans have been reclaimed for recycling, representing A$160 million in payments to the can-collecting public. Local councils and commercial scrap agents also accept large quantities of cans.

ALUMINIUM FOIL

Facts

Foil represents nearly 40% of the UK usage of **aluminium** in **packaging**, including beverage cans. Yet 50,000 tonnes of aluminium foil packaging is thrown away each year in the UK. Statistics from the Aluminium Foil Recycling Campaign show that 72% is single-material and collectable for recycling. This includes foil containers for convenience meals, pies and pastries, household wrapping and cooking foil, milk **bottle tops**, and chocolate foil. The majority comes from households rather than from the catering industry. The remaining percentage of foil is incorporated into multi-layer laminates, for example **cartons** (such as those used for milk or washing **detergents**), which are not suitable for collection at present.

Another large user is the cigarette and tobacco industry, consuming 29,000 tonnes of aluminium foil every year – or 38% of the total domestic foil consumption. In 1989, many millions' worth of foil was used in this way; much ending up as litter, destined for **landfill**.

With the imminent European Directive on Packaging – and the responsibility this places on producers to set up recovery schemes, the UK foil industry is already establishing pilot collection projects.

Reuse

Foil-lined gift boxes and presentation packs are classic examples of the overpackaging that fills so many dustbins/garbage bins. The mixture of materials – **paper**, **plastic**, and **aluminium**, often bonded together, makes recycling impossible. Always avoid buying such goods. Cut down on aluminium foil by using glass or pottery oven-proof dishes, and use greaseproof paper or reusable plastic bags (but not in the oven) for wrapping. If you do have to use foil, wash it in warm, soapy water and smooth it out for reuse.

Recycle

Collect torn foil, **bottle tops**, and aluminium food trays for fundraising charities. The foil must be clean for reasons of hygiene and to obtain the maximum remelt quality – and a higher price.

APPLIANCES See Electrical equipment, Kitchen utensils, Refrigerators, Tools, Washing machines

---

ASH
Facts
If you have an open fire, as much as 10% of the contents of your dustbin could be ash, soot, and cinders. And coal-fired power stations and industry produce millions of tonnes every year. With care, ash is reusable; pulverized ash is used by the construction industry as a component of concrete, or as a structural fill for projects such as London's Thames Flood Barrier (UK). In Germany, recycled fly ash is manufactured into energy-efficient concrete blocks. But the waste from **incineration** of municipal waste is much more tricky to deal with; bottom ash – the cinders that remain in the grate, can contain **heavy metals** such as **lead** and **cadmium**, while fly ash, which goes up the chimney and is hopefully trapped by pollution control equipment, has a larger surface area on which poisonous **dioxins** and PCBs can stick. In the US operators usually mix both types together, 36% goes to special **landfill** sites and 17% is buried in with normal landfill waste. What happens to the remaining 47% is unknown. Suggestions for reuse include construction blocks, road fill, and landfill cover – but only if the ash is properly stabilized to prevent heavy metals escaping.
Reuse
Mix small quantities of soot into your garden soil to help retain heat, and wood ash, rich in potash, to act as a fertilizer. This method is approved by the Henry Doubleday Research Association (UK).
Keeping slugs and snails off your vegetable patch is a never-ending task; a circle of ash or cinders around your plants might help. Add wood ash to **compost** heaps or to organic mulches such as leaf mould to make up for their initial acidity. Or make a cinder path in areas that get muddy quickly.

B

BAGS see Paper, Plastic

BAMBOO AND CANE

Facts

Bamboo, popularly known in Asia as the "poor man's timber", is a valuable resource providing food, shelter, medicine, and fuel for over 50% of the global population. In Asia, some species are so strong that they are used everywhere as scaffolding poles and construction materials. Because it is hard-wearing bamboo is popular for making furniture and antique pieces are still found at markets or auctions.

Rattans, a species of cane, are tall climbing plants, whose flexible branches are also used for furniture and woven goods such as **baskets**. **Chairs** made of plaited and woven rattan are an alternative to **timber**, although demand for some species now outstrips supply. Cane is a basic material for repair and restoration work.

Reuse/Repair/Recycle

Reuse bamboo canes as supports for climbing plants. Prevent cane furniture from becoming too dry and splitting by rubbing in linseed oil. If it is stained, use warm water and **detergent**, and then polish with a natural furniture cream – beeswax is good.

Mend second-hand furniture as soon as splits appear. Use **wood** or pieces of bamboo for minor repairs; in cane or wicker chairs, insert shaped pieces of wood into the crack and use a non-toxic **adhesive** to bind the pieces. Cane for reweaving is available in specialist art and craft stores. They will also advise on, or undertake, specialist repairs.

BASKETS

Facts

Basket-making is an ancient art using plant leaves or sinuous stems, woven or plaited into a variety of carrying or holding containers. Popular materials include canes, rushes, grasses and sedges, willow, raffia, plaited palm leaves in Micronesia, and tree roots. Many North American Indian designs incorporate feathers and beads. In parts of the world where the **plastic** bag is still a rare commodity, baskets woven from rushes are common for collecting and carrying food. In China these are often burned at the end of the day.

Reuse

Reuse baskets with broken handles for storing items around the house – logs, gardening equipment, **newspapers** and **cans** awaiting recycling, or fruit and vegetables in the kitchen. Also, line baskets with **plastic**, make a few slits for drainage holes, and plant with bulbs, flowers, or herbs.

Good craft shops sell replacement handles and repair materials, but it is much cheaper to mend soft, woven raffia baskets with the natural raffia found in most gardening stores. **See also** Bamboo and cane

---

BATHROOM EQUIPMENT AND FURNITURE

Facts

Baths were originally made from cast **iron** and coated with enamel. Although very heavy, cast iron is much more energy-efficient than **plastic** or fibreglass moulds, but it does tend to stain. Special renovation services do exist and some offer a colouring service for marked enamel (see Resources). Cast iron is always in demand as ferrous scrap metal.

Reuse

In the garden, old stone sinks make attractive plant troughs. If you want to make them look weathered, cover with concrete and rub some soil into them, lichen will soon appear. Natural yogurt is said to have the same effect. Alternatively make a small pond or water garden in a sink. When full they are very heavy, so make sure they are standing on a firm base. Old baths sunk into the ground make ideal ponds. Use old, broken paving stones, building rubble, or rocks around them to make a "crazy paving" surround.

Repair

Get scratches or chips re-enamelled. Some stains respond to lemon juice or, if necessary, a stronger proprietary stain remover. Find replacement taps at **salvage** or scrap yards, or try auctions for old-style fittings.

Recycle
Find out if organizations such as the Salvation Army or Goodwill Industries can use sanitary ware such as toilets and sinks (in good condition). Crushed porcelain from old toilet bowls is used in specialist tile-making in developing countries. Contact **scrap merchants** if you want to get rid of cast iron baths, and anything you cannot find a home for should go to civic amenity sites for appropriate disposal.

BATHS AND SHOWERS
Facts
Baths use far more water than showers; an average tub will hold up to 136 litres (30 gallons) of water compared to the 68 litres (15 gallons) of water consumed by a five-minute shower. Cut back on water use (and your heating bills) by showering and reuse as much bath or shower water as you can.
Reuse/Recycle
Greywater systems are not common or indeed legal in most places, but bath water is good enough for watering your garden, for washing down paintwork, and for cleaning the car. Set up a water collection system – buy or make a water butt to collect rain water or store used bath water. Save water by installing a toilet dam; a plastic bottle filled with water and placed in the cistern, away from the handle, has the same effect.

BATTERIES
Facts
Billions of batteries are used throughout the world – the US uses over 2.5 billion batteries every year. The throw-away type of batteries used in such appliances as **clocks and watches**, **radios**, shavers, and **toys**, are energy-inefficient and polluting once discarded. On average, a battery requires 50 times more energy to manufacture than it will ever produce as output. If you have to use batteries, buy rechargeable ones and a recharger. These can be used up to 1000 times before they wear out, but at present they all contain **cadmium**. The high-energy button types used in **cameras** and hearing aids usually contain high levels of **mercury**, and should be returned to stores for safe disposal. Some

manufacturers run battery recovery schemes whereby you can return spent batteries to the point of sale in exchange for new ones. Alternatively special collection bins are provided at some recycling centres for this type of hazardous household waste. Germany, Denmark, Switzerland, and Italy have separate collection systems. An EC Directive on safer battery disposal came into force in March 1993. For any schemes reclaiming waste for compost it is vital to keep batteries out of collected material. Keeping batteries out of domestic waste by placing a deposit on them may prove to be the only solution. In 1990 over 750 tonnes of cadmium were recovered from batteries; this could rise to over 1150 tonnes as more collection schemes are set up. A pilot project in the Netherlands, recovering 99% of cadmium from rechargeable batteries and commercial recovery began in 1992.

The lead acid battery is the most common type of rechargeable battery, from the type used in all cars and for energy systems on boats and caravans to the large stand-alone wind and solar systems. Nickel cadmium rechargeable batteries have very small capacities, but are useful for powering radios, small lights, and similar appliances.

When you throw batteries away with the rest of your rubbish they are likely to end up in a **landfill** site. Here the acids inside the battery dissolve out the toxic mercury and cadmium. In the UK, for example, about 14 tonnes of **lead**, eight tonnes of mercury, five tonnes of cadmium, and smaller quantities of nickel and manganese end up in **landfill** per year. There is a potential pollution problem if landfill sites leak into groundwater supplies.

Reuse

Reduce your dependence on batteries by plugging **electrical equipment** into the mains electricity supply (if this is possible). If you do have to use batteries, choose ones that do not contain harmful elements (see above) – most are clearly labelled. Consider switching to rechargeables, and reuse the sun's energy by getting a solar battery recharger. The time taken to recharge depends on the strength of sunlight, or the depth of discharge of the batteries. For the best results, recharge at the first sign of weakness. Batteries last up to four times longer when recharged after only a 50% discharge. Older batteries do become inefficient, and replacement before the end of their life is often necessary to keep equipment working at its highest efficiency.

Recycle
Find out if your local authority runs a separate collection service and, if not, ask if it has been considered. Use any facilities that exist and return car batteries to service stations for proper disposal.

BEDDING
Facts
Buy good-quality, natural fibres to reduce the need for replacements. Choose cotton without any fabric treatments – formaldehyde is used to achieve crease-resistance in fabrics, yet even in normal use, small quantities of vapour outgas from the fabric to irritate the respiratory system.

Reuse/Recycle
Make your own duvet covers out of old flat sheets or buy cotton-polyester sheeting (see **Thrift project**). Or try your hand at making patchwork quilts (see **Quilts**) from fabric remnants in sales. Use feathers from old eiderdowns as extra filling for sagging pillows or re-cover one. Search **jumble sales** for old feather pillows, after washing the feathers are fine to reuse for cushion stuffings. Small quantities of feathers can be put on your **compost** heap.

Extend the life of worn sheets by the traditional method of "sides-to-middling" (see **Thrift project**). Darn (see p.185) blankets using **wool** scraps kept from unravelling old woollen clothing, or for larger holes, patch with knitted squares. Give any unwanted wool blankets to charities for the homeless and needy, or to local animal refuges for bedding materials. **See also** Blankets, Mattresses

Thrift project
How to make a duvet cover
- Allow for the cover to be 5-10 cm (2-3 in) bigger than the actual duvet. Sew the two cover pieces together, right sides together, leaving a 1 m (3.28 ft) gap on one of the short sides.
- Pin self-sealing tape along each side of the gap and stitch.

Thrift project
How to "sides-to-middle" a sheet
• Cut through the hem and tear the sheet down the middle. Cut through the other hem.
• Overlap the two outer, unworn edges so that they now form the centre of the sheet. Stitch.
• Fold in outside edges and stitch to make new hems.

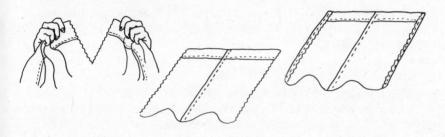

BICYCLES
Facts
Using a bicycle keeps you fit and is a non-polluting form of transport. Second-hand bikes are sold at second-hand outlets as well as at auctions, special sales, and through local newspapers. Unclaimed stolen property is also sold at such events – contact your local police station for details.

Many bicycle parts have other uses; use wheels for home-made handcarts or trolleys; bike lights as torches; carrying paniers as **baskets**; and nuts and bolts for general repair work. Repair workshops take unwanted bits and pieces – spare pedals, chains, frames, and so on. In India, Africa, and Latin America, old bicycle wheels are used as spinning wheels and as bicycle-wheel forges – the old inner tubes are used for the belt that drives the fan.

Reuse
Regular cleaning and oiling keeps rust at bay and most simple repairs are easy to tackle yourself. Buy a puncture repair kit and get a repair manual. Replace bent wheels or rusty pedals with parts from discarded bicycles – ask at a second-hand bike shop or check rubbish skips/ dumpsters at civic amenity sites.

BINDINGS FOR PACKAGING see Plastic

BLANKETS
Facts
Weaving blankets and **rugs** is a traditional art still practised throughout the world with looms made from scrap **wood**, and with **wool** respun from reclaimed fibres. Pure wool blankets are environmentally more desirable than synthetic, acrylic mixtures, which are based on a type of **plastic**. With good care, wool has excellent thermal properties and lasts for many years.

Reuse
Knit unwanted scraps of wool into blanket squares and sew them together to make a rug or **blanket**. Charities working with refugees, the homeless, and the needy will welcome unwanted blankets and bedding. Or take items to local animal shelters or **jumble sales**. Keep an old blanket in your car for emergency use.

Don't use or attempt to repair faulty electric blankets yourself, but seek professional help – unsafe electrics can kill. Thermal sheepskin or tufted wool underblankets are a safer option.

BONFIRES
Facts
Some people regard bonfires as an easy way of getting rid of garden/backyard waste, and bonfires are more common in areas where local refuse collections will not accept this type of waste in dustbins/garbage bins. But burning or incinerating waste is not recycling and bonfire smoke is a health hazard. (In fact the practice is banned altogether in Australia.) It contains approximately 70 parts per million of carcinogenic benzopyrenes – about 350 times as much as in cigarette smoke. These arise from the incomplete breakdown of cellulose in plants and make bonfire smoke a real hazard to those with chest or heart problems. Also present is poisonous carbon monoxide, one of the polluting gases found in vehicle emissions – burning one tonne of garden waste releases up to 30kg (66lb) of carbon monoxide.

In addition, putting damp material on bonfires lowers the temperature and releases more carbon monoxide. And burning certain types of **plastic** and synthetic materials releases hydrogen chloride, a toxic and corrosive gas, as well as poisonous dioxins from **PVC** (polyvinyl chloride).

Reuse

If you do have to burn waste, is it possible to reduce the number of bonfires? Are you burning a mixture of materials that could be disposed of in another way, or recycled? Are you burning materials that pose a hazard to you or your neighbours' health? Could you **compost** your garden/backyard wastes or gather **leaves** to make your own leaf mould?

Reduce woody waste by shredding or chipping – reuse the wood chips as a **mulch** to prevent weeds, or use as a path covering. Add small quantities to your **compost** heap.

If you do have to burn dry **wood** never burn old, painted wood or timber treated with wood preservatives – it might release **lead** and other noxious substances. Instead take the item to a civic amenity site for proper disposal. Bonfires on building (see **Building materials**) and **demolition sites** are a potential source of air pollution. Make sure old cans of **paint** and other chemicals are not burned. If in doubt, seek advice from your local waste disposal authority.

See also Building materials

BOOKS
Facts

It seems sacrilegious to try and destroy a book; surely someone, somewhere could use it! In any event, reuse is the best option since many latex-based **adhesives** hinder the recycling process. Until new water-based glues are more widely used, refrain from putting books in **paper** collections. And check with collectors about the recyclability of **telephone directories**.

Many more books than are at present could be printed on recycled paper. The US currently uses a greater percentage of reclaimed paper for books than the UK. And attention needs to be given to the bleaching processes used in papermaking; **dioxin** is a toxic byproduct of chlorine bleaching. **See also** Unbleached products

Reuse/Repair/Recycle
Buy from, and sell to, second-hand bookstores, or borrow books from libraries. Give unwanted books and magazines to friends, **jumble sales**, **charity stores**, and local community fundraising events. Organize a book sale in your community – involve your local library by getting them to help with publicity or by donating unwanted books. Reuse **wallpaper** scraps, decorative **wrapping paper**, **polythene**, or colourful fabric scraps (see **Thrift project**) to make protective book covers.

Antique books are valuable. Take them to reputable second-hand dealers and get several quotations before parting with them. Bookbinders undertake repairs, decorative restoration work, and rebinding with **leather** or fabric.

Thrift project
How to cover a book
- Cut the covering material 2.5 cm (1 in) larger than the book cover, with notches the width of the spine. Glue them flat.
- Glue the front flap to the book, then the cover, then the back flap. Trim the corners.
- Run a pencil along the spine to define the ridge.
- Glue the upper and lower flaps down.
- Glue the first and last pages down.

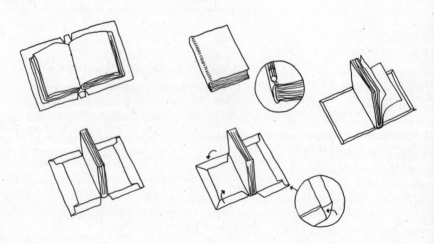

BOTTLES
Facts
Glass bottles have a distinct advantage over **plastic** ones as they are easy to refill (though at present such facilities are declining in some countries), and can be recycled repeatedly without any loss of quality. Reuse is always the best option, cutting energy and resource costs. In some countries, such as the UK, milk and beer bottles depend on maintaining returnable systems – these bottles are sturdier than one-trip containers, and can be refilled up to 30 times before recycling. **Bottle banks** are a popular collection method, but only because of a lack of any alternative, and bottles are usually broken up into **cullet** rather than kept whole.

Commercial bottle manufacture using 100% cullet has been done in plants in Thailand and in the US, and further developments are taking place in Japan, with the Ecology Bottle made from 100% cullet. Usually only 20-30% cullet is used to make bottles.

By comparison recycling schemes for **plastic** bottles are still in their infancy (see **PET**). Bottles made of polycarbonate can potentially be used, cleaned, and reused 100 times. Plastic is ten times lighter than glass – 20,000 plastic bottles weigh a tonne, compared to 2000 glass bottles. The actual process of recycling plastic is nine times more energy-efficient than making the original material from petrochemicals.

Getting people to return bottles after use is the key to maintaining viable recycling schemes. In many countries the demise of the returnable bottle is partly due to retailers' reluctance to operate returnable systems and an unwillingness on the part of manufacturers to use standardized containers. But renewed emphasis on waste reduction, as well as legislation, is giving returnables a much-needed boost. Deposit legislation in Denmark and some US states bans the non-returnable bottle. But elsewhere other **packaging** materials, including plastic, **aluminium**, or **steel cans**, and laminated **cartons** are increasingly substituted for **glass**.

In the developing world, glass bottles are always reused repeatedly. Selling bottles is for some people their only means of livelihood.
Reuse
Choosing drinks in glass bottles makes recycling easy; no glass containers should end up in your dustbin/garbage bin. Take all returnables back to the point of sale and reuse others by refilling with

home-made beer or soft drinks. Small, refillable glass bottles with twist-off/twist on metal tops can be used for bottling home-made herb oils or flavoured vinegars. Always label home-made items and never decant hazardous solvents or chemicals, including spirits and petrol, into breakable glass. Keep them in the original container.

Reuse plastic bottles (see **PET**). You can also make a cheap solar water heater with plastic bottles and black polythene sheeting: do-it-yourself instructions are available from alternative technology organizations (see Resources).

Recycle
Take all non-returnables to bottle banks or put out for kerbside collection. Encourage local authorities and the plastic reclamation trade to provide more banks for plastic bottles.

BOTTLE BANKS
If you cannot reuse **glass** bottles, the next best option is to recycle through bottle banks that accumulate the bottles as broken pieces (**cullet**). Bottle banks for **plastic** bottles are still in their infancy, but they do divert a certain amount of plastic away from the domestic waste stream, especially in areas which do not have kerbside collection schemes. Remove all metal caps and rubber seals. **See also** Bottles

---

BOTTLE TOPS
Facts
Apart from giving non-sharp bottle tops to children for using in craft projects, the only answer for small quantities seems to be the dustbin/garbage bin (larger amounts can be sold as scrap). In the process of manufacturing bottle or can tops, the circular tops are stamped out of a tinplate steel sheet. In Mexico, the remaining sheet full of holes (the "skeleton") is sold for reuse in the manufacture of air conditioners or filters, or for animal pens and cages.

Corks (see **Cork**) have a variety of household uses, and the lids from broken jam **jars** can be used as drip saucers for small plants, or upside down for standing small flower pots on – allowing water to drain freely away. **Aluminium foil** bottle tops are recyclable; keep for charity collections. Do not put metal caps in **bottle banks**.

BRICKS
Facts
In a recent survey the Building Research Establishment (UK) found that 9% of bricks delivered to building sites are wasted. Over-ordering, poor storage, and mishandling creates waste.

Reuse
Reuse good-quality, second-hand bricks from **salvage** yards or builders' skips/dumpsters for building work. They are not inferior in quality and are much cheaper than new ones. Weathered bricks also look better in garden walls, paths, and raised flower beds. Use traditional herringbone patterns for paths, reusing half or chipped bricks as edging blocks. Building brick structures for enclosing a **compost** heap or a barbecue pit are two more possibilities.

If you have unwanted bricks, contact a local builder's yard or recycling centre. Or make enquiries locally: an environmental or wildlife group may be able to use them. **See also** Building materials

---

BUILDING MATERIALS
Facts
Building work results in large quantities of waste, much of which could be salvaged for reuse. Better site management could cut over-ordering, reduce general mishandling, and improve the poor storage that renders materials useless.

Although the volume of demolition waste is huge, much of it is inert, allowing it to be crushed, processed, and reused as an aggregate in road building. But large amounts do end up as **landfill** rather than being recycled. In the UK, approximately 1.5 million tonnes of flat **glass** is wasted every year; retailers and demolition companies could help to recycle some of this. Illegal dumping (or **flytipping**) is common.

Waste containing half-used **paint** pots, discarded **wood** treatments, solvents, and chemicals is potentially hazardous. **Bonfires** on **demolition sites** are a source of considerable pollution. Building waste likely to be contaminated with asbestos must be treated as hazardous waste. Do not attempt to reuse it.

If you are professionally involved in the building trade, take care over the materials you specify for new developments or renovations. It is important that the materials do not contaminate the environment, the water supply, or add to the existing burden of pollution. In 1987 the number of different chemicals and synthetic substances used in the construction industry was estimated to be about 5000. Many substances are unrecyclable and difficult to dispose of. The building and construction industry is second only to the **packaging** industry in its use of **plastic**; in Europe it accounts for 20% of European consumption – over five million tonnes annually. The long lifespan of plastic makes it highly suitable for many applications: **window frames**, wall panels and cladding, flooring, thermal insulation, roofing, and all types of cable coverings. At present only about 10% of the plastic waste is recovered, although recycled plastics are extensively used in pipe-making; incorporating reclaimed plastic into road surfacing material and flooring is under way in Italy and Germany.

Wall boards made from recycled **newspapers** are coming on to the market, although supplies seem to be limited at present. Gypsonite replaces 15% of the crushed rock found in traditional gypsum boards with newsprint; the board is dent-free and strong. Fiberbond uses up to 40% old newsprint with perlite. CFC-free insulation boards from waste **paper** and formaldehyde-free **wood** fibreboard, suitable for furniture, **doors**, and general woodwork is also commercially available.

But using waste paper for building materials is not new. Throughout the world the very poor depend on waste paper as the construction material for their homes; its disadvantages have led to the development of asphalted roofing sheets made with the lowest grades of mixed waste paper and with a lifespan of five years. Small manufacturing plants exist in India and South America. Building materials are also retrieved from **cardboard** cartons, wooden crates, and demolition debris to build furniture, shelters, and workplace equipment. One Japanese company is now compacting rubbish into large bricks that can be coated in concrete and used in construction.

Reuse/Recycle

Look out for building sites near you – a small payment will often secure you the materials you want. There is a growing market for salvaged **timber** from old buildings and docks – listings of available timbers are found in architectural salvage indexes, or approach **salvage** yards directly. Office refurbishment schemes also yield timber, quality furniture, **carpets**, and **office equipment**.

Wood waste from building sites can be recycled or composted if separated from other materials. Commercial- size shredders reduce the volume of wood, but the end product is only ever be as good as the original material – if it contains contaminants – nails, screws, metal, or **paint**, it will not be suitable for recycling or composting.

Use pottery chimney pots as plant tubs; window frames for a garden cold frame, and discarded plastic piping for catching and directing rainwater into a water butt, or for making a makeshift irrigation system for your garden. Use broken stone or slate for paving or edging plant borders. Quantities of building rubble and old plaster dug into poor or heavy clay soils will help build a better soil structure. **See also** Demolition sites

---

BUTTONS AND BUCKLES
Facts
Before cheap plastic buttons flooded the world market in the 1930s, buttons resembling ivory were widely used by the fashion trade. These originated from the tagua tree – found in rainforest areas. A US firm has revived this practice; a fair trade contract has been negotiated with indigenous people in Ecuador to supply tagua palm buttons again. These buttons could become highly prized items within the fashion trade, creating a large, sustainable market.

Reuse
Over the centuries, **glass**, metal, **gold**, **silver**, shells, and china have all been fashioned into buttons. Antique fairs and street markets are still good hunting grounds for traditional buttons.

Before consigning old clothes to the ragbag, check whether you could reuse any of the buttons or buckles. Replacing buttons is a common repair job – collecting buttons in a button box could save both time and money, especially since prepackaged sets of buttons necessitates buying more than one or two replacements.

Thrift project
How to make button jewellery
- Twist one end of a piece of wire around a pencil, slide it out and clip the end.
- Thread on the buttons, making a pattern of different sizes, shapes, or colours.
- Close the open end in the same way.
- Loop pieces of ribbon through the wire loops and bind with thread.
- To make the closings, make a slip knot at one end and bind it. Make a fat knot at the other end.

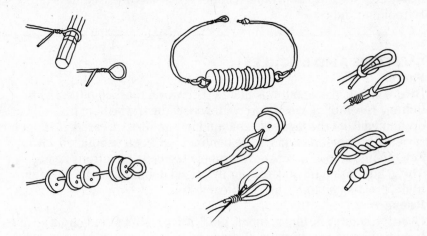

C

CADMIUM
Facts
Cadmium is a toxic **heavy metal** found in some industrial effluents, including sewage, and released by **lead** and **zinc** smelting and in the production of phosphate fertilizers. Cadmium accumulates in soil and water and is hazardous. Prolonged exposure damages internal organs and bones, and if inhaled death may occur.

Many **batteries**, including rechargeables, contain cadmium. Schemes for household hazardous waste, including cadmium-containing items, are common in the US, where **plastics** are the second-largest source of cadmium (28%) in municipal solid waste.

Cadmium is also found in colouring pigments – especially bright reds and oranges. The metal plating and vehicle industry is another source. The UK banned its use in food equipment in 1956 and Sweden and Denmark ban all cadmium-containing household appliances. Commercial recovery programmes are under way. An EC ban on the use of cadmium pigments by the end of 1995 is likely.

Reuse/Repair/Recycle
Avoid buying non-rechargeable, cadmium-containing batteries. Find out if there is a battery collection in your area – try recycling centres or contact your local authority, who may operate a household hazardous waste collection. **Paints** sometimes contain cadmium – check the label or buy non-toxic alternatives. Be aware that brightly coloured red and orange kitchen enamelware may contain small amounts of cadmium. In normal use this won't present any hazards, but if items chip or break do not attempt to repair them and stop using them for food preparation.
See also Batteries, Mercury

CAMERAS
Facts
The day of the disposable camera is here. Convenience is everything. No more fiddling with rolls of film, you just buy a **plastic** camera already loaded with film and after use send the entire package away for film processing. The throwaway cycle starts again with the next

disposable camera. But criticisms over the amount of plastic waste has led manufacturers into **salvage** programmes.

Reuse/Repair/Recycle

Don't be tempted to buy disposable cameras. Even if you only use a camera once a year for holiday snaps, it is still cheaper to buy an inexpensive or second-hand camera rather than a disposable.

When you upgrade your equipment, don't discard working cameras. Trade them in exchange for new equipment, or sell to second-hand, specialist stores. Give the cheaper types to children to experiment with or donate them to charity. It is helpful if you label items as still being in working order and write down technical information if you don't have the original instructions. If you do a lot of photographic work, including processing, it might be worth considering the possibilities of recovering the **silver** residue. For advice contact a specialist camera store or a commercial company involved in **precious metals recovery**.

Be aware that button-type camera **batteries** often contain high levels of **mercury**. Some stores accept them back for safe disposal. Or find out if your local authority runs a household hazardous waste collection.

CANS
Facts

Food and drinks cans are either made of tinplate **steel**, pure **aluminium**, or a mixture of both. Recycling rates vary. Every four out of five drink cans in the world are made from aluminium and 50% are collected for recycling. In the US, over 90% of drinks cans are aluminium and in 1989 60% of these 80 billion cans were recycled.

100 million steel cans are used every day in the US – enough to make a steel pipe from Los Angeles to New York and back again. In 1991 34% of steel cans were recycled (one in three). By comparison, the UK recycles just 10% of the 12 billion cans used each year. The Netherlands and Germany recycle over 45% of their steel cans and France has set a target of 50% by 1995. Their current rate is 30% and if their 50% target was achieved they would save enough energy to heat 4000 homes for a year. Australia is one of the world's largest recyclers of cans – 62% are recycled. Worldwide, the potential for recycling more aluminium and steel remains huge. It can be done. In mid-1992 recycling of metal beverage cans topped 90% in Sweden.

The production of 1000 steel cans (with a recycling rate of 30%) consumes 64kg (141lb) of iron ore, 25kg (55lb) of coal, 0.9 cubic metres of water, releases 171kg (376lb) of carbon dioxide into the atmosphere and consumes 2500 megajoules of energy. Substituting an aluminium can top with steel lowers carbon dioxide emissions by 53%. Overall manufacturing a steel can uses half as much energy as an aluminium one.

The environmental impact of not recycling is significant (see **Aluminium cans**). Recycling a tonne of steel cans saves 1.36 tonnes of iron ore and 3.6 barrels of oil. And energy savings of up to 76% are possible. The average US household consumes the contents of 4.5kg (2lb) of steel cans per week. When those cans are recycled enough energy is saved to keep a 60 watt light bulb burning for more than two days. Tin is needed in steel cans to stop rusting; detinning is a standard process prior to recycling that reclaims up to 80% of this valuable metal for reuse.

But recycling isn't the only way of saving resources. Today's cans are 40% lighter than 20 years ago. By "lightweighting" manufacturers are managing to achieve energy savings of more than 38% compared with energy use ten years ago.

Preventing cans from ending up as **solid waste** is the best strategy. For aluminium, this depends on consumers separating cans at source. Since steel is magnetic, there is the option of recovering cans by the installation of magnetic extraction plants at waste processing centres. These recover up to 80% of the steel, and can be used in conjuction with incinerators to extract steel from the ash. However such plants are costly and not all waste disposal authorities have them, so separating cans at source is still a sensible practice.

Within the developing world, the metal is a valuable resource and cans are frequently remanufactured into other products for resale. These include funnels, oil-lamps, and water containers in India and Nepal and embossed metalwork boxes in Peru.

Reuse/Recycle

If you cannot buy products in refillable or returnable packaging, the next best option is to cut waste by recycling all of your cans. Identify steel with a magnet by testing the body, not the top, of the can (aluminium is sometimes used here). If it sticks, it is steel; if it doesn't, it is aluminium.

Collection methods vary considerably from country to country – if in doubt, get in touch with your local environmental group or local authority. Encourage others to collect as well – some recycling schemes make a donation to charity for every tonne of metal they collect. If you don't have any recycling facilities, find out if your local authority extracts steel by magnetic extraction. If not, ask if a recovery scheme is planned.

Some can banks, such as "Save-a-Can" (UK), accept all types of can, separating them at the processing plant. Others take drink cans and may specify aluminium only. Food cans are generally steel. Rinse them out and recycle whenever possible or keep for kerbside collections. Squashing cans gives more room in the can bank, thus cutting transportation costs. **See also** Aluminium cans, Steel

---

CAR BOOT SALES see Jumble sales, Second-hand stores

CARDBOARD
Facts
In industrialized countries, about one-third of the contents of an average household dustbin/garbage bin is **paper** and **cardboard** and vast quantities of cardboard are wasted every week by retailers. Unless this material is separated at source for recycling, it ends up in the general waste collections and finally as **landfill** or waste for **incineration**. Generally, corrugated cardboard manufacturers do not accept cereal boxes or other paperboard products mixed in with clean cardboard unless they are recycling it into a low-grade filler material for new cardboard boxes.

Five billion new cardboard boxes are made annually in the UK from low-grade **waste paper**, cellulose, and **wood pulp**; all materials that are easily reused or recycled. Cardboard fetches a reasonable price, but the main drawback is its bulk; large volumes have to be collected to make recycling economically viable. And for retailers such as supermarkets and furniture stores, baling equipment is vital. Keeping plastic out of cardboard collections is important – the use of plastics and **laminates** is a big problem (see **Contraries and stickies**).

Recycling more cardboard rather than dumping it in landfill is one of the goals behind the US's move to setting "minimum content standards" for paper-based products. Legislation obliges US officials and contractors to use paper products containing a percentage of secondary fibre. Official buying has to favour recycled products. Overall, far more products could use recycled cardboard – both in primary packaging and for secondary, or transit, packaging – the boxes used to deliver goods to retailers. A large corporation has specified certain cardboard box sizes for all its suppliers; as items are unpacked the boxes are left uncrushed and are collected by a dealer, who sends them back to the company's suppliers for reuse. Another way of cutting waste altogether is to substitute crates made from recycled **plastic** that are returned for recycling. In Latin America, old corrugated cartons are turned into egg and fruit boxes.

Reuse

Reuse cardboard within the home; sturdy boxes make ideal containers for storing recyclables or items for the next **jumble sale**, or cut down boxes into filing containers for papers and magazines. Children's play groups or scrapstores have all sorts of creative uses for unwanted boxes. Or flatten them to save space, and keep for your kerbside collection, or take to recycling centres. Don't include any waxed or plastic-coated boxes, and avoid tying up with nylon string.

CARPETS

Facts

The **plastic** bottle of today could become tomorrow's carpet. Floor coverings made from reprocessed **PET** bottles are commercially available in the US. In general, the carpet industry already reuses a lot of secondary material; reclaimed textiles unsuitable for **clothing** are respun into hard-wearing carpet fibre. Adding mixtures of **wool** and synthetics such as nylon and polypropylene to carpets increases their ability to withstand wear and tear.

Carpets are not without their environmental hazards. Processing animal fleeces, the use of chemical treatments for mothproofing and colouring dyes cause pollution. From 1993, tougher European controls will limit mothproofing chemicals released into rivers; an alternative product derived from tree-bark extract is being tested in Germany.

Unlike wool carpets, synthetics do not need mothproofing, but the adhesives used to attach the carpet to the jute or polypropylene backing may "outgas" volatile organic compounds (VOCs). These give off a particular smell and are said to be responsible for the itching eyes and breathing problems some people face after a new carpet is fitted.

Carpets made from 100% undyed wool on a natural jute backing are becoming available – the manufacturers claim that minimum detergent is used to scour the wool.

Reuse

Choose the right type of carpet for the amount of wear it will receive. Pure wool is not as hard-wearing as mixtures of wool and synthetics. Keep spare pieces of carpet for matching paints and furnishings, repairs, or to use as doormats or **rugs** on heavily used areas. Also use carpet scraps to test that dyes are colour-fast before using shampoos and cleaners. Only use non-toxic, non-aerosol cleaning products. For spills, sprinkle with cornstarch and vacuum after 30 minutes. Carpets can be dyed, but worn, faded, or marked areas may give a patchy result and some foam-backed carpets cannot be dyed at all. So get professional advice from a carpet cleaning service and only consider dyeing if there is a lot of wear left in the carpet. Use up odd pieces of carpet and left-over scraps as kneeling pads for gardening, or use a piece as a cover for your **compost** heap.

Repair

Do minor repairs to extend the life of carpet that little bit longer. Sew or tuck fraying strands back into the carpet pile, and patch holes with spare pieces. If the carpet pile has become flattened by heavy trampling or furniture legs, try reviving it by pressing a warm iron over a damp cloth on the carpet – the steam will raise the pile. This is more effective on wool carpets than nylon and other synthetics. Alternatively seek professional advice from a carpet cleaning service. Using caster cups beneath heavy furniture legs will help stop pressure marks.

Recycle

Charities involved in helping the needy, or your local authority social services department are good places to try if you have carpet in good condition to donate. Because carpets are expensive items there is a big demand for second-hand carpets and rugs in good condition. Unwanted and worn out carpet should be taken to civic amenity sites.

CAR PRODUCTS
Facts
The various fluids used in cars – petrol, motor and gear **oil**, hydraulic fluids, anti-freeze, and others can be a significant source of potential pollution. Even routine car maintenance involves products that are potentially hazardous if the user disposes of them irresponsibly. Used motor oil, filters, anti-freeze, and brake fluid are poisonous and flammable, and car battery acid is very corrosive. Dumping such fluids down the drain is highly polluting and illegal in many places.

Reuse
Think about how you will dispose of the product before you buy it. Do you really need it? Buy only the quantity you actually need (buying in bulk is not a good idea) and find the least toxic product. You should keep leftover products in their original containers and you should not attempt to reuse or recycle **bottles** that once held chemicals. Give leftover products away rather than disposing of half-empty containers in household rubbish.

Recycle
Recycling is not possible for many car products. Ideally they should be collected for safe disposal – find out if a service station will accept them, or whether the local authority operates a household hazardous waste facility near you. **See also** Vehicle recycling

---

CARS
Facts
Every year approximately 11 million cars are scrapped in western Europe; 25% of their weight ends up in **landfill**, including over 620,000 tonnes of **plastic**, which complicates scrap recovery. In 1965 only 2% of the total weight of new cars was plastic, yet by 1990 this had risen to 14% – with plastic as a substitute material for **iron** and **steel** in car body panels and bumpers. Trends indicate that by the end of the century, up to 25% of a car might be plastic. Car dashboards and their **upholstery** also contain proportions of reclaimed textiles as a stuffing or filling material.

Car recycling schemes have to start tackling the problem of what to do with shredder residue, or "fluff", left over after metals have been recovered in the scrap process. Although a light-weight mixture of plastics, **paint**, **rubber**, and upholstery, the problem is the sheer quantity – the UK produces over 500,000 tonnes a year – and its potential toxicity from the **heavy metals**, PCBs, and hydrocarbons. The "fluff" is usually landfilled.

In Germany, the rising costs of landfill have led to proposals to curb waste by making the vehicle industry responsible for the waste it produces. The country currently produces three million cars a year, creating 75 million tonnes of waste a year – 25 tonnes per car. This is five times the amount of all their household waste.

While some European vehicle manufacturers are already funding pilot dismantling schemes, no such directive operates in Australia. Barriers to recycling include the sheer number of different materials and how to identify these. For example, two metal recycling companies in New South Wales smelter over 100,000 tonnes of cars per year, of which an estimated 70% is ferrous metal. The non-ferrous vehicle parts such as aluminium, plastic, and glass, have to be processed, cleaned, and categorized before being resold.

Reuse

Regular maintenance prolongs a car's life, reduces pollution and energy use, and cuts the impact of disposal. A UK study suggests that savings of 15% are possible if you check your car **tyres** and **oil** frequently. Increasing the engine efficiency cuts pollution; every year, the world's vehicles release over 550 million tonnes of carbon, as well as noxious pollutants, into the atmosphere. Check **scrap merchants** or **salvage** yards for spare metal parts or replacement upholstery.

Recycle

Dispose of unwanted **car products**, including **lead batteries**, anti-freeze, and used motor **oil** preferably through reuse or hazardous waste collections. Don't dump them. Have **tyres** remoulded if possible and try to find an alternative use for worn out ones. Old cars have a scrap value, or take them to a second-hand dealer. If you want a cheaper car, buy second-hand. If you aren't mechanically minded, take along someone who is, or get professional guidance.

CARTONS

Facts

The battle between the environmental lobby and the **packaging** industry over cartons has been a bloody one. Environmentalists claim that cartons are unrecyclable because of the mixture of materials used – paperboard, **plastics**, waxed **laminates**, and **aluminium** coatings. But the packaging industry maintains that cartons use minimal raw materials and that their shape and weight lead to savings on transport costs. Fears of **dioxin** contamination from the bleached **wood pulp** has led to further backlashes against the carton, and manufacturers were forced to adopt a more environmentally benign form of bleaching.

EC legislation has pressurized carton manufacturers to investigate and adopt recycling schemes. In Denmark 30 million **egg cartons** are made from recycled cartons each year. In Germany, Switzerland, and Japan, high-quality kitchen and **toilet paper** products made from recycled cartons are available on supermarket shelves, and trial programmes are under way in some countries, including the US and Germany, to manufacture a "chipboard" from post-consumer waste.

The light weight of cartons could prove a stumbling block for successful recycling schemes. Two million cartons weigh only 50 tonnes. A German firm has estimated that they will need at least 20,000 tonnes of discarded cartons per year to maintain a viable plant.

Reuse
Until recycling becomes possible, cartons are not reusable or refillable, so avoid buying them. Instead buy milk in returnable **bottles** and other items in refillable or recyclable containers. If you do have to buy cartons, don't discard them after use. They are sturdy and waterproof, and washed carefully can be reused for freezing small amounts of home-made soup or food left-overs.

CELLOPHANE
Facts
Transparent cellophane used for wrapping papers and **packaging** is made completely from cellulose **wood** fibre. Processing cellulose often involves chlorine bleaching, an environmentally damaging process. However cellophane packaging is biodegradable, harmlessly breaking down in between one and three years, unlike ordinary **plastic**, which takes centuries to partially disintegrate. In general, cellophane bags are regarded as environmentally acceptable; they are non-toxic and do not taint food, but because they tear easily their reuse is limited.

Reuse
Keep sweet wrappings for children's craft projects. Refill cellophane bags with purchases from bulk buying. **See also** Plastic wrapping

---

CENTRAL HEATING
Facts
Boilers begin to lose their efficiency after about ten years, yet most have an average lifespan of between 16 and 20 years. In the UK, more than three million homes have boilers that are more than ten years old. If these were replaced, approximately 5% of the UK's total domestic energy consumption would be saved, reducing emissions of greenhouse gases. Gas condensing boilers and proper insulation jackets around the hot water tank can make substantial savings on heating bills.
Reuse
Have boilers serviced regularly to maintain optimum efficiency. **Scrap merchants** readily accept old boilers, pipes, and radiators as scrap **iron** and **steel**.

CHAIRS
Facts
Upholstered chairs and **furniture** are frequently discarded when **fabric** coverings or **foam** fillings become worn. Unfortunately, the cost of repair and reupholstery can make replacing an inexpensive **chair** cheaper than having it re-upholstered or even recovered. As well as wasting a sturdy wooden frame, this situation does little to promote innovative furniture design for reuse. Chairs should have removable washable covers and replaceable fillings. In many developing countries rubber car **tyres** are cut into strips and woven into seating, or cane (see **Bamboo and cane**) and other traditional materials are used.
Reuse
Don't be tempted to buy new items that seem good value but cannot be maintained easily (i.e. without removable covers) – in the long run they only add to the overall burden of waste. Be aware that tropical timbers, including teak and mahogany, are popular for chair-making; buying such items means you are supporting an environmentally destructive trade.

If you are managing a tight budget, search second-hand stores and consider repainting or re-staining wooden chairs that seem past their best. A variety of non-toxic products is available (see Resources). A good hunting ground for chairs is rubbish skips/dumpsters, particularly those in smart residential districts or outside offices and buildings in the process of being refurbished.

Repair
If bamboo or cane chairs are damaged, either get replacement cane from craft suppliers or specialist stores, or take the chair to professional restorers. Have seats reupholstered as necessary; a professional job may be needed to achieve a good finish, but you may be able to sew a simple cushion or seat covers from canvas or a durable furnishing fabric. Or for an instant new look to damaged furniture, make some fitted covers or drape loose fabric or an ethnic rug over sofas. Refurbishment workshops that teach new skills to people with learning difficulties or the long-term unemployed may undertake cheaper repairs and accept all types of donated furniture for repair and resale.

Recycle
Give furniture to charity organizations for the needy, not-for-profit organizations, or to second-hand outlets. Or try selling more valuable chairs to antique markets. Some local authorities operate collection services for the disposal of unwanted bulky household items. Don't burn furniture with foam fillings – this gives off toxic gases. **See also** Upholstery

---

CHARITY STORES/THRIFT STORES
Facts
Every year charity organizations throughout the world recycle vast quantities of household articles. Much is reused in its original form, keeping useful materials out of **landfill** and incinerators. Some charity or thrift stores are high street names raising funds through resale of goods, while others work directly with the needy or homeless. Even small, seemingly worthless, things such as used postage **stamps**, foreign coins, and **wool** scraps can have secondary value. Your contribution may not seem large, but if everyone gives something and if schools and workplaces set up collections, useful quantities soon build and start to accumulate.

Reuse/Recycle

Instead of throwing items out, collect them for charity. The Salvation Army, Oxfam (UK), or Goodwill Industries (US) depend on people's generosity for goods for others to reuse. Find out what sort of items local stores need most; national charities will accept some materials (**aluminium foil**, stamps, etc.) by post. Ask others to donate unwanted goods. Reuse is always preferable to recycling, so take wearable clothes to charity stores instead of **rag** banks. Household appliances and **tools** are too valuable to throw away; some charities operate tool collection schemes for developing countries.

CHIPBOARD

Facts

This is a board manufactured from roundwood, sawmill residues, and other wood wastes. It is commonly used as an alternative to solid **wood** and has many uses – it can be covered in real wood or synthetic veneer for furniture, flooring, and other indoor purposes. In common with most bonded woodsheets, including plywood, chipboard releases small quantities of formaldehyde gas from the synthetic resins used in its manufacture. This can affect health, acting as an irritant to the respiratory system as well as causing headaches and depression.

Reuse

Reduce problems from formaldehyde by choosing other woods. Search **salvage** yards for seasoned solid wood or items you can take apart to reuse the wood. It is also possible to buy building materials, including waste-based fibre boards that do not emit this gas. Some are straw-based, others are made solely from compressed, recycled **paper**. If you cannot avoid using chipboard, keep rooms well ventilated and cut down on the use of synthetic solvents and **adhesives** used in repair work. Some of these are very toxic. If you are replacing chipboard furniture, keep shelving or open cupboards for garage storage.

Recycle

If you cannot reuse leftover wood, see if a local community organization has any use for it, or whether a salvage yard is interested in it. Or take unwanted and damaged board to waste disposal sites or recycling centres. Furniture restoration workshops and second-hand outlets are the best places for chipboard furniture. **See also** Timber

CINDERS See Ash

CLINGFILM/PLASTIC WRAP
Facts
Clingfilm, the thin, stretchy **plastic** wrapping used for food **packaging**, is a shortlife product made from a non-renewable resource. It is not biodegradable and limited reuse is only possible within the home; it is difficult to clean and often becomes tainted with the flavour of the food it has covered. Like many plastic wrappings, clingfilm is not readily recoverable when mixed with other municipal solid wastes.

Reuse
Avoid buying clingfilm – use greaseproof paper or put foods in airtight, reusable containers. Wrapping fatty foods such as cheese in **PVC** clingfilm has an element of risk. Plasticizers from PVC can migrate into the upper layers of the food; the health effect is unknown, but tests on animals have shown it to be potentially carcinogenic. Although non-PVC substitutes are widely available in supermarkets, research by the independent London Food Commission has found that many supermarket food counters still use the PVC type for wrappings.

[handwritten note: FOIL]

   Use **plastic bags** as an alternative – they are usually made from **polythene**. If you do want to reuse clingfilm, wash it thoroughly and, if it is very greasy, discard it.

CLOCKS AND WATCHES
Facts
These are generally long-lasting items that do not contribute much to the waste problem, although occasionally it can cost more to repair a clock than replace it. However you will need to think about the disposal of **batteries**, which often contain **mercury**. Ask a jeweller to accept them back for safe disposal or dispose through a household hazardous waste scheme or separate battery collection programme. An occasional oiling keeps mechanical clocks in working order; ask a jeweller or clockmaker to do this, or use three-in-one oil for the less fragile parts of most clocks. In general, clock repairs should be done professionally, but if a pendulum clock is running too fast or slow, simply correct it by altering the pendulum to the right length.

[handwritten note: WIND - UP Every thing]

CLOTHING
Facts
Every year in the UK millions worth of textiles (see **Fabrics and textiles**) are thrown away. Of the one million tonnes ending up in **landfill**, 400,000 tonnes are clothing. Discarded textiles now make up about 4% of the weight of domestic waste, in the US the figure is 5%.

This is a tremendous waste of resources, especially as the manufacture of many types of clothing creates significant impacts upon the environment. Converting raw fibres into finished fabrics consumes large amounts of water and energy, and for synthetics such as rayon, the process leaves a polluting effluent. In the UK the amount of clothing thrown away wastes the energy equivalent of three million tonnes of **oil** every day. To make matters worse synthetic garments are not biodegradable, giving them a lifespan of hundreds of years.

All garments are potentially reusable. In many developing countries well-established collection schemes exist, gathering unwanted fabric for recycling. This is a growth industry in India. And in the US and Europe, quality second-hand clothing is resold in thrift or **charity stores**, given to the needy, or sent by aid and development organizations to refugees and human support charities.

Reuse
Avoid buying clothes on impulse, and resist fashion items you are not going to get much wear out of. Reduce waste by buying good-quality fabrics that are repairable (see **Thrift projects**). An increasing number of companies are now producing clothing made with varying amounts of recycled fibre. Or look for unbleached cotton and undyed **wool**; harmful chemicals and manufacturing processes are not used, although untreated wool demands extra care to stop it matting.

Once or twice a year, sort out your clothes and donate unwanted items to charity or **second-hand stores**, or to **jumble sales**. Set up a swap shop with others – children quickly outgrow clothes.

If garments are too worn for repair, don't put them in your dustbin/garbage bin. Give to Oxfam Wastesaver, the Salvation Army, or St. Vincent de Paul for recycling; some charities run rag banks at recycling centres. Remove **buttons** and **zips** first for your own reuse, and keep

fabric remnants and wool scraps for repairs or patchwork (see **Quilts**).
Unravel old wool sweaters for reknitting.

Cut out your use of disposable paper towels by making cleaning rags
from old cotton clothing. Or be creative and make decorative bags and
rucksacks out of velvet or strong fabrics; make new clothes from old; or
cut clothes into strips and make a rag rug (see pp.225 and 230). **See
also** Fabrics and textiles, Rags

Thrift project
How to patch clothes
- Trim off the ragged edges of the hole and mitre corners.
- Fit a patch of matching or contrasting fabric (but similar in quality)
over the hole, turning in the edges. Stitch in place.
- On the other side, tuck edges of the hole underneath and slipstitch.

How to sew on appliqué patches
- Cut decorative appliqué shapes out of contrasting fabrics of similar
quality to the garment.
- Tack the patch in place on the right side.
- Using a thread as close as possible to the patch colour, sew the patch
to the garment with small overcast stitches, using the needle to roll the
edges under.

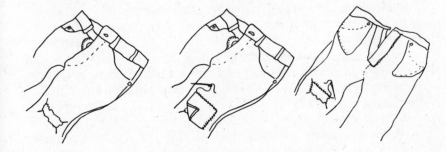

COMPOST
Facts

Approximately 30% of the organic matter in your dustbin/garbage bin could be recycled on a compost heap, or by **vermiculture**, using worms to produce compost. Composting makes it possible to garden without using chemical fertilizers, and is a traditional technique first used in China over 4000 years ago. Vegetable and food waste, as well as **paper** and light garden/backyard waste is transformed by bacteria and microorganisms into a rich, earthy soil conditioner, or **humus**. This is true recycling. In an age of deteriorating soil quality, when fertilizers from intensive cultivation deplete long-term fertility, waste-derived compost, including **sewage** sludge, can help to recreate fertile soils, preventing erosion.

Composting replenishes ecological cycles, as well as keeping organic wastes out of **landfill**. Decaying waste creates **landfill gas**, a major contributor to the greenhouse effect. Bacteria are the key to the successful recycling of kitchen and garden/backyard waste. They act by digesting organic matter (see **Organic waste**) into its basic elements to produce an earthy humus. In the right conditions, high temperatures build up within a compost heap, allowing bacteria to work faster. Other micro-organisms, including fungi and tiny insects, assist the decomposition process.

Besides vegetable and garden waste, other compostible materials include: sewage sludge, straw, **wood** chips, and municipal solid waste. Home, or backyard, composting, is common in the US; compost bins are provided at low or no cost. Participation rates are high where there are ongoing educational/publicity schemes, and incentives to recycle.

Composting schemes are well under way in Denmark, Germany, the Netherlands, and the US, where "Compostibles at the kerbside", doorstep collections, are increasing. In Italy the agricultural use of waste-derived compost is seen as the logical way of restoring organic matter to the soil in intensively cultivated areas. **See also** Leaves, Sewage, Shredders, Soil additives, Vermiculture

Thrift project

How to make a compost heap

- Build a holding area with bricks or salvaged wood in an unused spot.
- Start the heap on a pile of woody prunings to ensure good air circulation. Build up with vegetable and garden/backyard wastes, adding suitable food scraps that won't attract rodents (i.e. fat and meat). Avoid using diseased materials, seeding material, and perennial weeds such as dandelions, which could root. Mix grass clippings with woody prunings to maintain a good balance of nitrogen and carbon-rich materials.
- Turn the heap over occasionally to speed up the decaying process. A wooden lid or a piece of old carpet on top will help keep the rain out and the heat in.

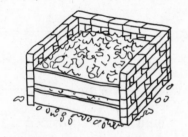 

Make a compost tumbler

Make a rotating barrel composter for a fraction of the commercial price. Ask at factories, builders' yards, or service stations for unwanted barrels – 250 litres (55 gallons) size is ideal. Cut a loading door in one side and hinge it, making sure it fits tightly. You may need to prime a metal drum. Construct a wooden or metal frame to allow rotation (search skips/dumpsters for suitable materials).

Use a compost trench

"Pit and trench" composting follows a three-year rotation of soil incorporation of food wastes, growing crops, and pathmaking. In the first year dig a trench, fill it with food wastes (avoid meat and animal products) and cover it. Use the rows on either side for growing crops and as a pathway. Change the uses the next year, and the year after. Then start the cycle again.

Use a Green Cone
The Green Cone is a commercially available composter which uses the sun's rays and natural organisms to turn food waste (including meat, fish, and bones) into compost. Bury the Cone partially in the soil and fill it with waste. Move it around the garden/backyard to give a nutrient boost to different areas.

Compost troubleshooting

Symptoms	Problem	Solution
Bad odour	Pile too wet – not enough air	Turn compost – add woody stalks and other coarse material
Pile is dry	Not enough water – too much woody material	Turn and mix in fresh grass clippings or fertilizer, chop up woody wastes

COMPOST TOILETS
Facts
Flushing the toilet is one of the biggest water-users in the home; each flush wastes litres of high-quality water. We have an "out-of-sight, out-of-mind" mentality about **sewage**, yet for centuries it has provided a valuable fertilizer or soil amendment. Conserving water and recycling nutrients is the aim of compost and waterless toilets. Although designs vary they all work on the principle of composting human excrement into a pathogenically safe soil conditioner (see Resources). They are particularly suitable for homes without mains water supply or those reliant on cesspits or septic tanks. **See also** Nightsoil, Sewage

COMPUTERS
Facts
In the computer industry technological change is rapid and the potential for waste is enormous. Companies discard hardware for more user-friendly equipment, advertising pressure to upgrade computers is incessant, and spare parts for standard machines are increasingly hard to get. One multinational company is now operating a computer collection and recycling scheme to recover precious metals and other

valuable components from the printed circuit boards. According to the US Environment Protection Agency personal computers are in active use for only 20% of the time they are switched on, and 30–40% are actually left on overnight. A major manufacturer has designed an energy-saving device that makes the computer enter a "sleep" state when not in active use.

Reuse

Not-for-profit groups are always short of office equipment, so consider donating your unwanted equipment. Ideas for reuse extend to all the accessories and supplies you need for computer work. Computer listings **paper** is a high-grade product, suitable for use as a direct pulp substitute in the papermaking process. Throwing it away should not be an option (see **Paper**).

Computers do not generate printed words without a printer and maybe a photocopier. Most laser printer cartridges and ribbons are refillable or reusable so check whether your office supplier has details of reinking services. Inkjet cartridges can be refilled.

Recycle

A well-known computer giant has begun a "design for recycling" initiative. Plastic components are to be labelled with the resin type and the manufacturer. They also plan to launch a computer with a high recycled-materials content.

CONTRARIES AND STICKIES (CONTAMINANTS)

Facts

One of the greatest problems hindering waste **paper** recycling is contaminants, particularly **adhesives** and **plastics**. If a certain proportion of these are present in post-consumer waste, the paper is unsuitable for reuse, and if they reach machinery, will cause damage.

Examples of items which must be kept out of paper collections include all types of plastic waste, including window **envelopes**, coated paper, waxed **laminates** (for example, **cartons**), and metal linings or embossed papers. Latex **rubber**, the adhesive used by printers and bookbinders, is also a problem. It is found in self-seal envelopes.

Reuse/Recycle

Help your local recycling collections by careful sorting. If you aren't sure whether something can be recycled, either leave it out or ask.

Including it in a bundle of otherwise suitable material is not a responsible action. If you work in the printing trade, find out if your workplace will convert to water-soluble adhesives.

COOKERS/STOVES
Facts
Electric cookers/stoves are one of the biggest users of electricity within the home; a microwave oven cuts electricity use by 50%, since cooking times are much shorter. By comparison, a typical gas cooker/stove uses less primary energy, generating 80% less carbon dioxide – a greenhouse gas – than its electric equivalent. In the UK an electric cooker/stove costs about three times as much to run as a gas cooker/stove.

Cookers/stoves are termed "**white goods**" and are made primarily of recyclable **steel**. Reconditioning them and thus extending their working life saves far more energy than dismantling them for steel scrap.
Reuse/Recycle
When you have the oven/stove on, maximize energy use by cooking several dishes at once, or use the grill instead. Toasters use less energy than electric grills.

When you need to replace your electric cooker/stove, switch to gas if possible. It is probably not worth replacing cookers/stoves (and other white goods) with new, more energy-efficient equipment until they are worn out. The energy implications of scrapping working equipment are substantial. It is better to get the full use out of an existing item and then get a trade-in price on a new piece of equipment. When buying look for energy labels or check product information. On trade-in deals, old equipment is either sold for reconditioning or sent for scrap. Alternatively take working appliances to **second-hand stores**, refurbishment workshops, or recycling centres. Many charities for the homeless accept white goods.

COPPER
Facts
Copper was one of the first metals to be used by humankind. It is

valuable and has a good scrap value. Recycling only requires one-tenth of the energy originally used to process virgin copper ore, and is important for reducing the polluting extraction method. Copper mining, refining, and smelting cause substantial industrial air and water pollution; much of the world's supplies come from developing countries, including Peru. Here out-of-date equipment is responsible for vast quantities of sulphuric acid gas emissions, with over 200 times the permitted level being recorded in the atmosphere.

Copper is popular for kitchen equipment because it is an efficient conductor of heat. This makes it a valuable metal within the electronics and building industry. It is also used in metal **alloys**; **tin** and **copper** makes bronze, and **zinc** and copper produces brass. Nickel **silver** is actually an alloy of copper, nickel, and zinc.

Reuse

Any copper that is likely to come into contact with food or liquid should be coated with tin, otherwise a poisonous green rust, or verdigris, forms, making items dangerous for use. Have the tin or silver linings of **saucepans** renewed every three years if pans are in regular use. Many specialist kitchen stores operate such a service.

Keep a good shine on copper with a solution made from equal measures of salt and vinegar in warm water. Treat copper surfaces as if they were non-stick and do not scour them. Repair work or resurfacing is a job for a professional metalsmith as copper has to be softened before working. Copper scrap – wire, **building materials**, and pipes – fetches a high scrap price.

CORK
Facts

This is a wholly natural product made from the outer bark of the cork oak of southern Europe. Between 55% and 60% of the world's cork comes from Portugal. At present there is enough cork to meet world demand; the traditional regime of stripping the trees once every nine years is maintained, yet cork suitable for wine bottles only appears after the third stripping – about 43 years after the tree was planted.

Every year about ten billion corks are used as **bottle** stoppers, but few are reused. Corkboard is produced from any factory waste and ground cork granules are used in the manufacture of **linoleum**.

Despite the use of **plastic** as a substitute, there is renewed interest in cork as a non-toxic, hard-wearing material with a variety of uses, including flooring, **tiles**, and wall coverings (see **Wallpapers and wall coverings**). Cork makes an excellent insulation material in the home.

Reuse

Reuse corks for children's projects; for bottling home-made vinegars and herb oils; as knife tip or skewer protectors, and put them on the end of eye-level bamboo canes in the garden to prevent accidents. Shred them and use the pieces for mending small gaps in cork floors.

Many cork tiles are treated with synthetic substances or backed with **PVC** to prolong their life. Such products may emit low levels of chemical vapours that irritate the respiratory system. Instead use non-toxic products as a sealant (see Resources).

CULLET

Facts

Cullet is the broken glass emptied from **bottle banks** or broken **glass** arising from the manufacturing process. Although glass can be continuously recycled without losing quality, the main incentive for recycling is to cut energy costs. Every tonne of cullet used in a furnace saves the energy equivalent of 135 litres (30 gallons) of oil and 1.2 tonnes of primary raw materials. In Europe, some companies use up to 90% cullet in their green glass furnaces, substantially cutting demand for sand, soda ash, and limestone; the raw materials of glass-making.

At bottle banks, putting bottles into the right colour compartment is important; brown and green glass have different chemical compositions – mixing them produces a lower-grade glass. Mixed cullet is used in green furnaces. Demand for the different types of cullet varies with market conditions, but getting the public's recycling behaviour right from the start is important.

Excess cullet is used for fibreglass manufacture (an insulation material or for lightweight structures such as water tanks or boats) and incorporated in road asphalt. In developing countries, cullet is extensively reused in manufacturing **bottles** and **jars**, in **jewellery** and bead-making, and for handicrafts. It can be incorporated into **mosaics** or decorative **tiles** for walls and floors.

Reuse
Reusing bottles or jars by refilling is always the best environmental option. Why smash a sturdy bottle into pieces, use energy to transport the cullet to a glass processing factory, use more energy to remelt, reform and refill it, and finally to complete the cycle by transporting it to the retailer and consumer? Bottle banks are the last option and returnables should never be put in them. **See also** Bottles, Glass

---

CURTAINS
Facts
Sunlight fades and eventually weakens fabric; curtain linings prevent this and thick (especially thermal) types help prevent heat loss. Although some fabric treatments prolong life or increase resistance to stains, they contain chemicals that can release irritating vapours. Anyone with asthma, should avoid treated fabrics.
Reuse/Recycle
Many curtains are discarded before they are worn out because of changes in fashion, so always choose quality fabrics in a timeless style or pattern that won't date. Reuse old curtains as protective drapes when painting and decorating, or use for children's play projects. Buy fabric remnants in sales or search **jumble sales** and antique markets for hardly-worn cast-offs and alter them to fit your windows. Or make linings for existing curtains and use existing scraps for patchwork (see **Quilts**), bags, or cushion covers. Give your unwanted curtains to **charity stores**. **See also** Fabrics and textiles

---

CUTLERY
Facts
Maintain cutlery by regular cleaning and sharpening; straight-edged **knives** can be reground at home, using a whetstone or knife sharpener. Serrated knives need specialist equipment, so take them to a knife grinder or hardware store. Metalsmiths are able to restore and replate worn **silver**. Auctions and antique markets are sources of second-hand silver and most buy unwanted items. Don't throw away bent forks or spoons; keep them as small gardening implements for seedlings. **See also** Knives, Kitchen utensils

D

DECKCHAIRS
Facts
The canvas parts of deckchairs and director's chairs are liable to rot and split after a few years' use, or sooner if stored when damp. The frames may still be in perfectly good order.
Reuse/Repair
Hardware stores and furnishing fabric departments of large stores sell replacement lengths of striped or plain canvas, or plastic for repair work (see **Thrift project**). If you don't want to tackle this yourself, ask where you could get repairs done. Give unwanted chairs to **charity stores** or to **jumble sales**.

Thrift project
How to replace deckchair canvas
- Buy a new length of canvas the same length as the old (allow about 50 mm (2 in) extra for turnings) and tacks. Fold one end under 25 mm (1 in) and tack it around the top rail. Hammer the tacks right in, starting from the middle and working outward.
- Repeat for the other end, but taper each side until it fits. Line up the edge of the fold with the inside edge of the rail underneath.

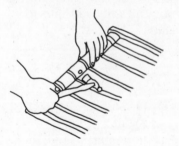 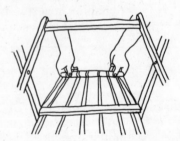

DEMOLITION SITES
Facts
Demolition sites and building restoration schemes create large amounts of waste. In the UK, more than 125 million tonnes of rubble is landfilled every year. Over two million tonnes of aggregrate is consumed; 50% of this is potentially recyclable.

Building practices are such that reusable materials become mixed with rubble, stone, and soil, reducing their value and making recycling difficult or uneconomic. This waste material is then only suitable as infill for construction work, or as **landfill**.

In an attempt to curb growing volumes of waste, the construction industry is investigating ways of identifying reusable materials. Labelling and the use of bar codes are being tested. But ultimately reducing waste means adopting more selective practices at demolition sites. **Salvage** schemes for **timber** and similar materials are gaining popularity, and you can buy high-quality materials and old fixtures and fittings from architectural salvage indexes or salvage yards.

Reduce/Reuse
If you are involved in any demolition work at home or in the workplace, find out what is happening to the unwanted materials, and if they are of value, whether there is a particular second-hand market. **Bricks**, paving slabs, and soil may be reused for rebuilding, or constructing raised flower beds and garden paths. Classic-styled wood-panelled **doors** add more interest to rooms than many modern designs, or convert them into items of furniture. A solid wood door makes an ideal workbench, or table. **Aluminium** or steel **window frames** do not rot; use them to replace old wooden frames or make a cold frame for growing seedlings in your garden. Alternatively, sell or give metal frames to **scrap merchants**. **See also** Bricks, Building materials

Thrift project
How to make a garden cold frame
- Use a wooden or metal window frame with glass still intact, or improvise with thick polythene sheeting.
- Build a square structure out of spare bricks, with one end higher than the other. Use half bricks or wood to fill in the gaps and put a sand or gravel layer in the bottom of the frame to assist drainage.
- Place the window frame over the top.

DETERGENTS
Facts
Cleaning products prolong the life of materials, restoring them to their original condition. But many products are manufactured with petroleum-based substances, as well as containing added whiteners, brighteners, bleaches, and other unnecessary synthetic substances. These may help the product to clean items faster, but the price to the environment is high.

Water pollution is common; petroleum-based products biodegrade slowly and sometimes incompletely, leaving substances that are toxic to fish and plants. In addition petroleum reserves are limited. It is more appropriate to leave them as a source of energy, especially when vegetable oil-based products are effective substitutes. Such products also biodegrade much faster.

Water quality is affected by phosphate use, used as a water softener. About 30% of the phosphorous discharged into Australia's waterways from sewage treatment plants is from detergents, or about 20% of the total amount of phosphate discharged. Phosphate was considered the major cause of the world's largest outbreak of toxic blue-green algae; a 1000-km (621-mile) stretch along the Darling River in 1991–2. Alternative products are minimally packaged in recycled cardboard or recyclable polyethylene plastic bottles.

DIAPERS see Nappies/Diapers

DIOXIN
Facts
Dioxin is one of the most toxic chemicals ever made. It is known to cause cancer, birth defects, and sterility, as well as affecting the immune system and the liver. Dioxin accumulates in the body's fatty tissue and can reach babies through breast milk.

The paper industry is potentially a major source of dioxin, through the chlorine bleaching of **wood pulp**. However, consumer awareness has made tremendous impact upon the industry, forcing manufacturers to adopt safer oxygen bleaching processes. In Sweden 96% of **paper** products, including **nappies/diapers**, are now chlorine-free. But

demand from countries such as the UK for bright-white products
means that Sweden is still producing chlorine-bleached pulp for export.
Reduce
Buying unbleached paper products is the best environmental option.
Look for items such as **toilet paper**, coffee filter papers (although it is
cheaper to buy a reusable cotton or metal filter), **nappies/diapers**,
and writing paper.

You also need to beware of burning treated **wood** or **PVC** sheeting
on **bonfires**; this can release small quantities of dioxins. **Incineration**
as a waste-disposal method can pose similar hazards if sufficiently high
temperatures are not reached.

DISPOSABLE GOODS (DISPOSABLES) see Nappies/diapers,
Shortlife goods, Toilet paper

DOORS
Facts
Old doors often end up in demolition waste or on rubbish skips/
dumpsters from office refurbishment schemes or home renovation
work. Many of these could be easily reused, restored, or recycled into
useful new items.
Reduce
If you have to replace rotted **wood**, do not buy substitutes made from
tropical **timber** and reduce hazards by only using toughened **glass** in
doors. Search **salvage** yards for replacements, but make sure you buy
the correct size. A badly fitting door allows a surprising amount of heat
to escape from the building.
Reuse
Instead of replacing doors that are still in good condition, think about
repainting or revarnishing them. Strip wood doors back to the natural
wood; seek advice before you use blow torches or dry-sanding
equipment on old paintwork. It can release lead particles, so you must
always wear a facemask and work in a well-ventilated room.
Alternatively, get professional help; companies often use caustic soda
baths for stripping large items such as doors and furniture. Make a
workbench in your garage from an old door; use shelves, old kitchen

cupboards, wooden tea chests, or **bricks** as the supports. Alternatively, put a hinge on the door so that it can be folded away on to a wall after use, saving space.

Repair/Recycle

Oil the hinges on creaking doors regularly; rehang a warped door; and for doors that stick, plane or sand the offending side. Mend cracks in doors by either using new wood or preparations such as plastic wood filler. If you cannot give old doors away, take them to civic amenity sites or recycling centres for scrap.

DRAUGHTPROOFING MATERIALS

Facts

Draughty buildings waste energy. In the home about one-quarter of all heat may be lost through badly fitting **doors** or windows. Gaps in floorboards are another problem. Fitting durable draughtproofing materials could cut your heating bills by 15%, and insulation materials for your loft or hot water tank will quickly pay for themselves.

Reuse

One of the easiest ways of excluding draughts is to fit **plastic** or metal draughtproofing strips to the bottom and sides of doors. Special adhesive foam strips around door frames or windows also help. A long doorstop, made from leftover fabric remnants or wool squares, and stuffed with old **tights/pantyhose** (see **Thrift Project**), will help stop draughts. Heat also escapes through the letterbox; you can buy draught excluders or use a heavy piece of **carpet** and make your own. Lined **curtains** help keep the heat in as do heavy curtains over doors or windows – but don't cover radiators with curtains – heat is lost. Fill gaps in floorboards with small strips of wood or rolled up sheets of newspaper; this also forms an extra insulating layer under carpets. A DIY form of double glazing can be made with **plastic** sheeting or even plastic **clingfilm/plastic wrap** stretched over **window frames** and attached with double-sided adhesive tape. Lightly blowing the surface with a hot hair dryer will smooth out wrinkles. It is important to leave some natural ventilation – completely airtight homes are dangerous because of the possibility of a build-up of toxic fumes. **See also** Insulation materials

Thrift project
How to make a draught-excluder
- Cut two identical strips of hard-wearing fabric, such as corduroy or denim, the width of the door plus seam allowances and about 15 cm (6 in) wide plus seam allowances.
- Place right sides together, stitch the two long edges and one short.
- Turn right sides out and stuff with old tights and fabric scraps until the excluder is solid and heavy.
- Hand-stitch the remaining seam from the outside.

DRINKS CANS see Aluminium, Cans, Steel

DUSTBINS/GARBAGE BINS
Facts
The variety of collection systems for rubbish, and the existence of recycling schemes, have made it necessary for different types of waste receptacles, including compartmentalized bins or plastic rubbish sacks, to be manufactured. Separating waste from recyclables is made easy with the "split-bin" system, common in many parts of Europe. Different-coloured bins are used for "wet" (organic) and "dry" (**glass**, metals) wastes. "The Blue Box" system, keeping recyclables out of rubbish altogether, started in Ontario, Canada, more than a decade ago. By April 1991, 2.7 million Ontario households had kerbside, multi-material "Blue Box" systems and the idea has spread to many parts of the US and Europe. Several pilot schemes are under way in cities in the UK. Many of the dustbins/garbage bins and boxes used in these waste minimization trials are manufactured using recycled **plastic**.

However providing one large, wheeled dustbin/garbage bin for household refuse has, in the UK, been found to have an adverse effect at "drop-off" recycling sites. With such a large dustbin/garbage bin, which also takes garden waste, people are not bothering to separate and return recyclables.

Lack of space in the home for storing recyclable items is often given as the reason for not recycling. In future, it is vital that kitchen designers start to consider "design for recycling". The layout of the kitchen and its furniture will have to provide built-in space for recycling boxes and the small dustbins/garbage bins for collecting items such as food waste for composting.

Reduce/Reuse
If you find you have a spare dustbin/garbage bin after you have cut down the amount of materials you throw away, convert it into a worm bin (see **Vermiculture**) or use it for composting (see **Compost**), or paint it and plant it with small shrubs or trees.

Separating materials at source doesn't necessarily need special bins or boxes. If kerbside collections operate in your area you will be issued with a plastic box. Otherwise reuse an old tea chest, or a discarded milk crate for storing **bottles**. A sturdy **cardboard** box, with its bottom reinforced, will be quite adequate for dry wastes. Make recyclable drinks **cans** take up less room by crushing them with a small rubbish compactor or a heavy foot.

DYES
Facts
Dyeing can give a new lease of life to "tired" clothes and fabrics, but most commercial dyes contain chemicals rather than being based on vegetable or plant extracts. The ones to avoid are black, navy blue, or dark-shaded metallic dyes. They are not biodegradable and can be hazardous if they reach groundwater supplies. Other coloured dyes take a while to biodegrade, but are not a long-term hazard.

Effluent from commercial dyeing processes can cause pollution; fixatives (mordants) such as chrome and alum are added to make sure the dye adheres to the material, and cotton and linen are routinely bleached to ensure even colouring.

Reduce
Look for natural plant and vegetable dyes (see Resources) or make your own. Commonly used plants include marigolds, camomile,

sunflowers, black currants, and imported dyestuffs such as indigo, walnut husks, and coffee beans. Tea leaves give a stain which lightens with time and lichens are popular for colouring wool. Instruction books are available; try your local library or branches of organizations such as the Association of Guilds of Weavers, Spinners and Dyers. Tie-dying and batik are both ancient dyeing crafts (see **Thrift project**), which are easy to do yourself at home.

Reuse/Repair

Old buckets and **saucepans** bought at **jumble sales** are ideal for dyeing fabrics, alternatively use a **washing machine** or the bath. Always read the manufacturer's instructions fully before starting; not all fabrics, especially synthetics, are suitable. Refurbishing **carpets** and **rugs** by dyeing is possible.

Thrift project

Simple tie-dyeing

- To make a simple sunburst design (for example, in the centre of a plain white T-shirt), take hold of the centre of the piece to be dyed and allow the rest to hang down.
- Starting at the centre wrap rubber bands or string tightly around the fabric, leaving intervals. The tied areas will remain white while the rest is dyed.
- Dip the fabric into the dye. Hang it up to dry. Remove the bands or string. To achieve a multi-coloured effect redye when dry, but put the bands in different places.

Simple batik dyeing

- Melt down beeswax from candle stubs, add a little paraffin and brush on to the fabric (or use special applicators, available from specialist craft outlets). The waxed areas of your design will remain white, while the rest is dyed.
- Dip the fabric into a dyebath and soak it thoroughly in the dye.
- Remove from the dye and hang to dry. When the fabric is dry, melt off the wax using an iron and absorbent paper.
- To redye the fabric, using a second colour, repeat the process, but apply the wax to different areas.

E

EGG CARTONS
Facts
Traditionally egg packaging was made from environmentally benign, low-grade recycled pulp before the widespread introduction of **plastic**, foam-blown egg cartons. Prepackaging has led to the decline of the returnable egg carton. Although most plastic cartons are CFC-free, the substitute chemicals used to "blow" the foam still affect the ozone layer. The plastic is difficult to recycle and is not biodegradable.
Reuse
Choose recycled pulp cartons in preference to others and find outlets that accept them back – try markets, free-range egg sellers, farms, and small holdings. Or reuse them yourself as biodegradable starter pots for seedlings; the transparent (non-biodegradable) plastic type with a lid is like a mini-greenhouse. Children's playgroups can reuse all types.

EIDERDOWNS see Bedding, Quilts

ELECTRICAL EQUIPMENT
Facts
All logical waste reduction programmes involve cutting back on energy and water use in the home or workplace. Domestic and industrial electrical equipment is often energy-intensive and inefficient. In the US, offices use 30% of the nation's electricity; leaving photocopiers, printers, and computers switched on when not in use costs American businesses billions worth of electricity every year. Better design of appliances, with energy-saving switches, cut-out devices, and automatic timers reduces unnecessary waste.

The energy efficiency of the average domestic appliance in the UK is well below that of the best mass-produced models in Europe and North America. In these countries **refrigerators** and **washing machines** generally use at least 20% less energy and 25% less water. Energy labelling is compulsory in the US and Canada and common in Australia. Other electrical equipment includes power tools, **garden/backyard**

equipment, and **lighting**. If a householder replaces normal incandescent bulbs with low-energy lighting, the equivalent of one tonne of carbon dioxide (a major greenhouse gas) is kept out of the atmosphere over the lifetime of the bulb.

Reduce
The most energy-efficient appliance is the mechanical one you operate yourself – the energy bill is zero, except for your own. Stop using unnecessary electrical equipment – the electric toothbrushes, the kitchen carving knives, and other "timesaving" devices. Many are bought on impulse; some are invaluable, but others are quickly discarded when they break or are found to be too fiddly to clean properly. Ask about the energy efficiency of products, and look for energy labels.

Reuse
Buying reconditioned **vacuum cleaners, cookers/stoves**, or **refrigerators** saves you money and prevents items still in working order from going on the scrap heap. However be aware that the large users of energy – refrigerators, **washing machines**, and cookers/stoves, may actually consume more energy than new models. In the long run, the initial financial saving may be cancelled out by increased electricity bills.

Repair
Unless you really know what you are doing, it is not safe to make repairs, even temporary, to electrical equipment yourself. Instead take goods to a reputable repair store, refurbishment workshop, or find out if the manufacturer offers a repair and annual servicing facility.

Unfortunately, too many products now have "built-in obsolescence" and may not be able to be repaired because vital parts are no longer manufactured. It may be possible to cannibalize parts from another machine, so get a second opinion.

Recycle
Donate unwanted but functioning equipment to **charity** or **second-hand stores**. Older equipment, such as refrigerators, need careful disposal (see **Refrigerators**). Motors and compressors contain hazardous PCBs, which escape into the environment if equipment is crushed. It is essential that PCB-containing parts are removed prior to scrapping for **steel** – take disused equipment to reputable scrap dealers. **See** Kitchen utensils, White goods

Typical power consumption of electrical appliances (240V)

Appliance	Average wattage
Battery charger	20
Blanket (under)	60-120
Cooker/stove (oven and hob)	12000
Computer	30-100
Convector heater	1000-2500
Dishwasher	3000
Drill	250-500
Fan (heating)	2000-3000
Food freezer	300-700
Immersion heater	3000
Iron	1250
Kettle	2500-3000
Microwave	600
Oil-filled radiator	500-2500
Radiant heater	500-3000
Sewing machine	75
Spin drier	300
Storage heater	2000-3000
Television (black/white)	50
Television (colour)	100
Toaster	1050-1360
Towel rail	30-1000
Tumble drier	2500
Vacuum cleaner	500
Video recorder	110
Washing machine	2500
Water heating	1000-5000

The generation of 1 kilowatt hour of electricity from a coal-fired station produces 1 kilo of carbon dioxide (CO_2)- a major greenhouse gas. 1,000 kilos = 1 tonne

(a kilowatt hour = 1,000 watts of electricity supplied for 1 hour or a 100W bulb lit for 10 hours)

(Source: Wind and Sun Safe Energy Suppliers 1991)

ENVELOPES
Facts
Sending a sturdy new envelope through the post every time we write a letter is wasteful, even when brown manilla envelopes contain recycled paper. In most businesses, reuse is not an option. There's an underlying feeling that it does little for a company's "slick" image to be sending out envelopes that have already been used. Some companies collect them for waste **paper** collections, but the problem of contaminants from the **adhesives** used in self-seal envelopes (see **Contraries and stickies**), the plastic in window envelopes, and metal clasps or staples mean that many envelopes just get put straight into the **dustbin/garbage bin**.
Reuse
At home and work reuse as many envelopes as you can. Use a paperknife or letter opener, and reseal with special envelope reuse stickers or plain labels. Use the backs of envelopes for lists or reuse at work for internal mail. Find out if your company has investigated multi-user envelopes; each time the envelope is received, the recipient simply crosses out the last address and reuses it.
Recycle
In the workplace find out from your paper collector what can and cannot be recycled, and start collecting.

F

FABRICS AND TEXTILES
Facts
Between 3 and 5% of the weight of domestic garbage is discarded
textiles: everything from **rags**, cleaning cloths, worn out **clothing** and
outmoded fashion items to household furnishings and old **carpet**. Too
little is kept out of the **dustbin/garbage bin**, although all kinds of
fabrics have a host of industrial applications if recycled. The
upholstery trade is a major user of flocking and stuffing, while many
industrial processes rely on wiping cloths made from unwanted textiles.
But fabric reuse is the best option. Oxfam's Wastesaver Scheme (UK)
for example, wastes nothing; anything that is still wearable is either
kept for selling in their outlets in the UK, or sent abroad to refugees
and developing countries, allowing others to have access to cheap
sources of high-quality clothing.

Many traditional arts and crafts – for example patchwork, **quilting**,
and rag rug-making (see **Rags**) grew out of economic necessity; and
are once again becoming popular as interest grows in finding ways of
reusing the wealth of fabrics ending up in **jumble sales** or worse still,
in the **dustbin/garbage bin**.

Recycling and reprocessing fabrics into new clothing is hindered by
the finishes and treatments now applied by the textile trade. In
addition, many of the substances used for cleaning and processing
leave a polluting effluent or cause air pollution. Formaldehyde is added
to cotton to make it crease-resistant, the effect is long-lasting, but so are
the side effects. In use, traces of vapour are slowly released and these
can cause allergic reactions, particularly in asthmatics.

Reduce
Reduce waste by choosing good-quality fabrics for clothes and for items
that have a long lifetime – **bedding**, quilts, **curtains**, and other soft
furnishings. Cheap fashion clothes may not turn out to be the bargain
they first seemed – holes quickly appear and repairs are difficult.

Reuse
Ask textile retailers for unwanted fabric swatches or sample books for
use in schools or playgroups, or for making patchwork quilts or bags,
or tie-dye and batik projects (see **Dyes**).

If clothes are too worn for repair, cut up and reuse the fabric for patches (see **Clothing**) or to make smaller things. Children can make hand puppets out of fabric scraps or old socks (see **Thrift project**). Save money by using scraps as dusting and polishing cloths; or as cushion stuffing. Use left-over canvas, poplin, linen, or stiff fabrics to make a window blind; improvise by using the fittings and poles from a broken blind, or make your own with a pole and some nylon cords.

Repair
Prolong the life of fabrics by doing repair work as soon as necessary; patch small tears with the same fabric or make colourful contrasting patches for children's clothes. Strengthen areas such as knees and elbows before holes appear. Keep **zips** and **buttons** from old clothing put in rag banks for repair work. Always use non-solvent based **adhesives** for repairs.

Recycling
As well as rag banks and **charity stores**, another way of recycling is to give fabrics remnants to children's play schemes or to **scrapstores** – many depend on factory offcuts of textiles, leather, and wool as materials for creative projects. **See also** Clothing

Thrift project
How to make hand puppets
Using an old, brightly coloured sock or two shaped pieces of scrap fabric sewn together, sew on two buttons for eyes, fabric scaps for ears, and wool scraps for hair, beard, or moustache, depending on the character you are creating.

Thrift project
How to make soft juggling balls
- Mark out a six-segment cross shape on squared graph paper – each segment should be about 5 cm (2 in) square.
- Using the graph paper as a template, cut out from the fabric, allowing an extra 1 cm (½ in) all round for turnings.
- Fold in the turnings around the template and tack in place.
- Using invisible nylon thread oversew the sides together to form a "box", making sure that corners are secure. Then sew up two of the remaining three edges of the "lid".
- Undo the tacking stitches and take out the template.
- Fill the "box" with lentils or rice, stuffing in as many possible.
- Stitch up the remaining seam.

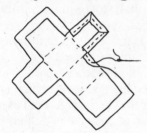 

FERROUS METALS
Facts
Worldwide, **iron** and **steel** are the most important ferrous (iron-containing) metals recovered by the scrap reclamation trade. During the last ten years over 2.5 billion tonnes of steel have been recycled back into steel products. In the UK this activity saves over ten million tonnes of finite raw materials, ten million tonnes worth of **landfill**, and 1.4 billion gallons of petrol (energy equivalent) every year.

The amount of ferrous metal in domestic waste varies, but the average amount is 6-8%, mostly in the form of short-life packaging, especially tinplate **cans**. Steel is magnetic (**aluminium** is not) so it is easy to separate steel cans from your waste for recycling. Waste disposal authorities use magnetic separation equipment to extract steel from solid waste; barriers to more recycling include the lack of such

equipment. The UK has just 25 plants (1992). Bulky **white goods –
refrigerators, cookers/stoves** and **washing machines**, and
electrical appliances yield vast quantities of recyclable steel every
year and **demolition sites** are valuable searching grounds for scrap
dealers, local "totters", and **salvage** merchants.

The standard 200-litre (45-gallon) **oil** drum is a valuable scrap
commodity in any country, but there are lots of ways it can be reused –
as a container for liquids or food, as a water butt, as a waste bin, as a
small incinerator or temporary furnace, or cut open to make an animal
feeding trough, or converted into a cheap **compost** tumbler. In
developing countries oil drums are never wasted. Some are even
flattened by throwing under the wheels of a heavy, moving lorry. The
resulting metal sheet is used for vehicles or as a building material. Cut
down, they are converted into buckets and small stoves and the round
ends are fashioned into cooking or washing bowls.

In all developing countries, ferrous scrap is made into a multitude of
products including tools, horseshoes, iron manhole covers (with
tinplate cans in the mix) and machine parts. In Peru, there are
examples of metal gates with attractive lattice-like patterns, which are
the result of stamping electric motor parts from steel strips. And using
a furnace, ferrous scrap can be converted into decorative bench ends,
coffee grinders, shelving brackets, weighing scales, stoves, shoe lasts,
wheels, and vehicle parts.

Reuse
Instead of giving old sinks and cast iron baths away, keep them as plant
troughs or make a small garden pond (see **Bathroom equipment and
furniture**). Iron and steel rusts (stainless steel, an **alloy**, does not) so
you will need to add a protective rust-proof coating first. Use steel cans
with smooth edges as pencil holders or for storing nuts and bolts.

Recycle
Recycle all steel cans and take unwanted appliances or vehicles to scrap
yards for dismantling. **See also** Iron, Steel

FLYTIPPING
Facts
This illegal practice of dumping unwanted waste, often of building or
demolition waste, as well as bulky household items on roadsides or

vacant land is a major problem in towns and cities. Although some waste could be reused, the rest is often too mixed or contaminated to be of value. Rising disposal charges encourage some disreputable companies to try to reduce their operating costs by dumping their waste, often at night. There are no official statistics for the scale of the problem, but tackling it is costly; London authorities spend millions every year removing waste from the capital's streets. But flytipping isn't just building waste; in rural areas the sight of rusting **cookers/stoves**, dumped **cars**, mattresses, and **tyres** is common. Flytipping encourages a throwaway mentality in others, and, as well as its nuisance value, it can be dangerous to people and to the environment, especially if industrial waste is dumped.

Reduce/Recycle
In an effort to control flytipping some local authorities publicize a special telephone number for members of the public to report incidents to the relevant authorities. If you see anyone behaving suspiciously, try to take the vehicle registration number and report it to the police

If there are sufficient recycling facilities, including home pick-up services for unwanted bulky goods and skips/dumpsters regularly placed in the streets, the temptation to dump should be reduced. If you have items that cannot be repaired or resold, take them to a local authority disposal site.

FOAM
Facts
Plastic foam is found everywhere – from **upholstery** fillings to the **packaging** "chips" used to protect fragile equipment from damage in transit. Foam **polystyrene** packaging is extremely difficult to recycle, often ending up as litter, and some still contains ozone-damaging CFCs. Even packaging made with the so-called safer substitutes is thought to have an effect on atmospheric gases. Fast food outlets and drink dispensing machines daily use large amounts of disposable plastic foam packaging. Pilot recycling schemes are under way – for example "Save a Cup" collection schemes – but the light weight means that huge quantities are needed to justify transport and reprocessing costs.

Paper is often seen as an acceptable substitute for the catering industry, but waxed papers act as **contraries**, hindering the recycling process. Fears over possible traces of **dioxin** in paper products has led manufacturers to adopt safer pulp bleaching methods, and to promote unbleached products.

Another type of foam is latex from natural or synthetic **rubber**; this is less hazardous than the polyurethane (plastic) foam found in some upholstery and mattress stuffing. This has now been banned because of the serious fire risk from matches and lighted cigarettes; less combustible foams are now used. But the hazards remain in second-hand furniture, an alternative stuffing is a horsehair mixture, although this is expensive.

Reduce
Avoid using foam packaging and cups. If your workplace uses foam cups take a pottery mug to work, and encourage others to do the same. If your workplace has drinks vending machines, investigate the possibilities of collecting **plastic** cups for recycling. There is no real use for packaging foam "chips" except reusing them. Write to manufacturers suggesting they switch to shredded paper, straw, recycled pulp or **wood**-based products. Return **egg carton** packaging for reuse, or use as starter pots for seedlings. Do not burn unwanted foam upholstery – this can emit toxic fumes. Instead take to a civic amenity site for proper disposal.

FOIL see Aluminium foil

FOOD/FOOD WASTE
Facts
Uneaten food and fruit and vegetable peelings account for a significant proportion of domestic waste. It is estimated that Americans dump the equivalent of over 21 million shopping bags full of food into **landfill** sites every year. Not only is this an inappropriate use of space, but the transportation consumes energy and decaying food produces a potentially polluting liquid, **leachate**, as well as **landfill gas**.

In the UK, putrescible organic matter (including garden waste) accounts for 25-35% of the weight of household waste. Wasting less in the first place by improved storage, only cooking what is actually needed and using leftovers, or freezing them, are important practices.

Inedible waste should go on to the **compost** heap, or dig a compost trench for oily or meat food scraps, or compost using a Green Cone (see **Compost**). Fruit and vegetable waste is quickly turned into a crumbly soil conditioner if you buy or make a worm bin (see **Vermiculture**). Commercial outlets such as restaurants, markets, and food stores daily throw away large volumes of food waste – there are no statistics. But in a world of inequitable food supplies, throwing away so much is both unethical and environmentally unsound. Composting schemes are on trial in parts of the US.

Throughout the world many food production systems are based on reusing resources; in many parts of Asia, aquaculture – backyard fishponds – provide a constant and cheap source of protein. Tilapia and Grass Carp have been specially bred for this purpose. They feed on low-grade vegetable matter, so they can be fed kitchen wastes, such as vegetable peelings, fruit and coffee grounds, and in Asia adding **sewage** is practised. Growing fish in solar ponds or in warm water effluents from industry is also common – Tilapia are resistant to high levels of pollution.

Another system is hydrophonics – growing plants without soil and nourishing them with water and fertilizer solutions. In Bengal, households grow rice organically, using manure shells or pots filled with animal dung. These are sunk into the growing containers, nutrients are slowly released, and the rice flourishes. But these are not just developing-world practices; reusing waste and human sewage, after processing with anaerobic digestion is being used in many appropriate-technology and self-sufficiency developments.

Reduce
Reducing the overall amount of waste your household produces is probably the most important action you can take. And precycle to cut the amount of **packaging** materials you bring into your home. Buy organic fruit and vegetables and eat the peel; if this is inedible (for example, citrus peel), grate it and dry lightly in the oven and then use it as a flavouring in cake mixtures. Make nourishing soups from the outer leaves of vegetables and leftover food scraps. Don't buy more food than you know you can eat, freeze any surplus or leftover food, and compost as much organic matter as you can. And don't forget that pets often appreciate a bowl of scraps. Waste disposal units that grind up and flush food wastes away are not recommended.

Reuse
If you have a freezer, use it for leftover food, or freezing seasonal foods.
Donate quantities of leftover, but still edible, perishable food to
charities supporting the homeless, or to residential children's homes.
Although this practice is largely carried out by retailers, there might
still be occasions, such as formal dinners or workplace events, where
caterers over-estimate quantities of food. Try to identify possible outlets
in advance – for example, contact organizations such as the Salvation
Army, who run soup kitchens for the homeless in urban areas.

FOOD CANS see Cans

FREEZER see White goods

FRIDGE see Refrigerators

G

GARBAGE BINS see Dustbins/garbage bins

GARDEN/BACKYARD EQUIPMENT
Facts
Don't be tempted to buy the latest gardening gadgets – instead buy a
few multi-purpose tools of the best quality you can afford and extend
their life by regular cleaning, sharpening, and careful maintenance. A
wipe with an oily rag is a simple way to prevent rust. Share equipment
with neighbours and hire occasionally-used items such as hedge
trimmers, shredders, and other power tools.
Reuse
Many common household items can be used as garden/backyard
equipment. Make a cold frame from a discarded **window frame**; raise
seedlings under a cloche made from a disused aquarium; use **glass jar**
lids for raising flower pots off the ground, or cut down **plastic bottles**.
Make plant troughs from wooden fruit crates. Line them with plastic,
cut drainage holes, and fill with soil. Or make a propagating unit from a
fruit crate covered in plastic sheeting. Commercially, recycled
materials are already used in some garden/backyard equipment.
Manufacturers of **compost** bins and plant tubs incorporate varying
proportions of recycled **plastic**, and several companies manufacture an
imitation **wood** made from reclaimed post-consumer plastic waste. This
is rot-proof, does not need wood preservatives, and is made using a
material which would otherwise be wasted. Another recycling idea,
adopted by a UK company, is reusing imported fruit barrels to make
compost tumblers.
When you buy seedlings in plastic pots or polystyrene seed trays,
remove the plants carefully and use the containers for next year's
seeds. Even better, avoid buying pots by reusing yogurt pots, **tin cans**,
empty paint cans, and **egg cartons** as starter pots for seedlings. Use
cracked china and pottery dishes as plant saucers or as small bird
baths. Give tarnished or bent cutlery to children to use as small
gardening tools. And keep bent forks for planting miniature bottle
gardens, weeding alpine rock gardens in converted sinks, or for

handling seedlings when repotting. Drill a hole in empty paint pots and fill with trailing plants and suspend them as a hanging basket.

Search skips/dumpsters or building sites for discarded wooden pallets or metal **oil** drums and convert them into low-cost composting equipment (see p.137). Discarded fruit boxes come in all shapes and sizes and wholefood stores often have the long, narrow fruit boxes, which make ideal window boxes, especially as a herb garden on a kitchen window sill. Drill a few holes for drainage in the bottom.

Repair

Mend split hoses by cutting out the split sections and rejoining with a waterproof tape, or cut a series of little holes in the plastic and lay across the soil surface or lawn as a drip irrigation system (see **Thrift project**). This is a water conservation technique providing a constant trickle of water across a large surface.

It is worth buying a knife sharpener or whetstone for keeping a sharp edge on knives, but power tools or lawn mowers are best resharpened by an expert. Specialist tool repair workshops restore all types of equipment; your local garden centre may offer these services, or look in the telephone directory.

Recycle

Good second-hand markets exist for many garden/backyard tools, but if you are not worried about getting a price for them, give to charities such as Tools for Self Reliance (UK). They operate a network of local groups which collect and refurbish tools; tool sets are made up and sent to developing countries, where appropriate items are always in short supply. Alternatively, donate unwanted equipment to tool-sharing schemes; tool libraries; sell them at car boot sales; or give them away for dismantling and spare parts. Reasonable quantities of **steel** are always accepted by **scrap merchants** or **salvage** yards.

Thrift project
How to make a drip sprinkler
- Make small holes along the length of a discarded hose.
- Lay it across the grass, potted plants, or bury it in the flower bed.
- Connect it to the mains water supply, or water butt and turn on gently so that a gentle trickle comes through. Or use it as part of a greywater reuse system.

GARDEN/BACKYARD WASTE
Facts
Gardens/backyards are a major source of domestic biodegradable waste. Grass clippings, leaves, dead plants, and hedge trimmings are all organic materials with a variety of further uses. Keeping this organic matter out of **landfill** reduces the build-up of methane gas and other undesirable substances. In the US, many states ban the landfilling of garden/backyard waste. Instead, centralized municipal composting facilities accept material and householders are encouraged to participate in backyard composting programmes. Free bins are sometimes provided as an incentive.

Reuse and recycling is central to organic gardening practices; composting, shredding, chipping, or mulching are preferable methods of dealing with waste. Manure can be applied directly to the soil to provide nutrients as it biodegrades.

Reuse
Build a **compost** heap. Seek guidance from organic growing organizations or from groups (see Resources) on the best methods of dealing with different types of garden waste. Unless it is very wet or cold, leave grass clippings on the grass – they quickly recycle nutrients back into the soil. Gather fallen **leaves** and make your own leafmould, and deal with woody stems by hiring a small shredder or **wood** chipper – these efficiently convert wood wastes into **mulch** or wood chips. **See also** Bonfires, Landfill gas, Vermiculture

GLASS
Facts

Glass forms about 10% of dustbin/garbage bin waste (by weight) in the average western household. Yet most glass containers are recyclable if you separate them from the rest of your rubbish. Reuse is always the best environmental option, cutting the costs of manufacturing a new **bottle** or **jar**, thus saving energy and resources. As a result of deposit legislation, returnable bottle systems are common in parts of Europe, including Denmark, and some US states ban the use of non-returnable containers. Industries that still place a great reliance on returnables include the dairy trade for milk bottles, and breweries. With Australians purchasing over 800,000 tonnes of glass per year, effective recovery systems are imperative.

After refilling, recycling is the next best option. Collections through **bottle banks** are well established in many countries. In Australia some 260,000 tonnes is recycled per year; about 40% of the total amount purchased. The big recyclers are the Netherlands (70%), Belgium (55%), Switzerland (71%) and Germany (63%). Even Turkey, which also has a well-developed network for returnables, manages to recover more glass from bottlebanks (28%) than the UK (21%).

A major advantage of glass compared with **plastics packaging** is that recycling produces a high-quality product, even when it is continuously recycled. But the main incentive for reclaiming glass from household and commercial waste is to cut energy costs. Recycling one tonne of waste glass (**cullet**) saves the energy equivalent of 135 litres (30 gallons) of **oil** and 1.2 tonnes of primary raw materials. One tonne of glass is equal to 2000 bottles. Each tonne of cullet produces a saving on the energy required for melting the glass of 36kg of fuel oil (1.5 gigajoules) and a saving on the energy required to produce primary raw materials of 60kg of fuel oil (2.5 GJ) The overall total energy saving is 100kg of fuel oil (4 GJ).

Although glass is made from raw materials that are relatively cheap and plentiful – sand, soda ash, and limestone – quarrying them has a significant impact on the surrounding countryside. Recycling glass reduces this problem and keeps bulky non-biodegradable glass out of **landfill**. If bottles and jars recycled through UK bottle banks in 1991 were laid end to end, they would go around the equator three times. Some countries reuse up to 90% of waste glass (**cullet**) in new bottles and jars, the UK average is 20%, but it can be increased to 80%, depending on the type of glass being made.

Throughout history, scrap glass has been reused in many other ways – melted down to make glass beads, cut into shaped pieces for stained glass objects, or used for embellishing **mosaic** designs on walls or flooring. Renewed interest in junk art and design is reviving many of these traditional crafts. Glass can also be reprocessed into a number of new materials; it can be substituted for quartz or feldspar in the manufacture of high-strength porcelain pottery; or used to make mineral wool, an insulation product; and incorporated into construction materials including road aggregrate.

European Glass Recycling 1990

Country	Tonnes Collected	Shares of National Consumption
Austria	156,000	60%
Belgium	223,000	55%
Denmark	60,000	35%
Finland	15,000	31%
France	987,000	41%
Germany	2,295,000	63%
Great Britain	385,000	21%
Greece	26,000	22%
Ireland	16,000	23%
Italy	763,000	53%
Netherlands	360,000	70%
Norway	10,000	22%
Portugal	50,000	30%
Spain	310,000	27%
Sweden	57,000	44%
Switzerland	199,000	71%
Turkey	54,000	28%
Total	5,666,000	40.9% (average)

Source: British Glass 1992

Reuse

Reduce waste by choosing returnable glass bottles whenever you can, and buy recyclable glass instead of plastic. Some wholefood stores offer a refill service for products such as juice concentrates. Don't put returnable milk or drink bottles into a bottle bank; returnables have thicker glass walls to withstand the rigours of transport and rewashing. Instead return them to the point of sale for refilling. Milk bottles can be reused up to 30 times before being recycled.

Keep non-returnables separately for kerbside collections, or take to **bottle banks**. Don't make a special car journey for this – you might end up using more energy than is actually saved by recycling. Combine trips to the bottle bank with shopping or travelling to work. Or, take it in turns with neighbours. Wash glass containers thoroughly before storing, and remove metal lids and caps. Try to reuse glass jars rather than putting them in a bottle bank, and don't put broken window glass, light bulbs (see **Lighting and light bulbs),** or heatproof kitchen equipment into any bottle collection scheme. This glass is made from different materials and cannot be recycled along with ordinary glass. **Salvage** yards may accept old **window frames** with the glass intact or convert into garden equipment such as cold frames and cloches. **See also** Bottles, Bottle banks, Cullet

---

GOLD
Facts

Half the world's gold comes from the CIS and South Africa, but mining operations are environmentally destructive; cyanide is used in processing the ores and water pollution is common. Gold is a soft precious metal, so **copper** and **silver** alloys are frequently added to increase its resistance to everyday wear and tear. Other metals, including silver and platinium, are used as substitutes, and gold leaf, an alloy of copper and **zinc**, is used for craft work such as restoring faded decorative metalwork, antiques, books, sculptures, and church fittings.

Reuse/Repair/Recycle

Gold has a very high scrap value and there is always a market for old, hall-marked jewellery. On the industrial scale, small quantities of gold are recovered from the printed circuit boards used in electronics, computers, and telephone systems. Many manufacturers accept this type of equipment back for extracting the precious metals and useful components, and there are specialist precious metal recovery companies for other products. **Jewellery** stores undertake repairs, including restoring gold-plated items – this has to be done professionally.

GRASS CLIPPINGS see Garden/backyard waste

GREEN MANURE
Facts
You can help nature fortify the soil by growing "green manure" plants. Clover, mustard, and lupins are all fast-growing varieties that are extremely beneficial to the structure and fertility of the soil. Some plants in the Legume family, including clover, are able to "fix" nitrogen in the soil; this is a vital ingredient for healthy plant growth.

Too many of our agricultural and horticultural systems stretch the capacity of the soil beyond reasonable limits. Continuous cropping, often highly dependent on pesticides and artificial fertilizers to maintain and maximize yields, results in impoverished soils. Globally, soil fertility will continue to diminish unless more sustainable practices, including organic farming, are widely adopted. Every year the world's farmers lose an estimated 24 billion tonnes of topsoil from their croplands.

Reuse/Recycle
Buy "green manure" seeds from seed catalogues, garden centres, or from organic gardening organizations (see Resources). Permaculture groups also offer advice on sustainable growing systems.

Sow seed on "resting" land or after harvesting main crops. When the plants reach maturity, dig them into the soil; here micro-organisms and bacteria break them down, releasing their valuable nutrients. The leaves of some species, including comfrey, are also suitable as a **mulch** material, or for adding to your **compost** heap. Alternatively cut the leaves up and put them into water butts collecting rain water from the roof. This type of liquid manure makes an ideal feed for potatoes, tomatoes, and bean crops. **See also** Manure, Mulch, Soil additives

GREYWATER SYSTEMS
Facts

Conserving water and making maximum reuse of waste water is the basis of greywater systems. Water from baths, showers, and sinks is collected for irrigating the lawn or garden/backyard, and for activities that do not require water of a drinking standard – car-washing, flushing the toilet, and so on. "Black water" – used water from toilets and greasy water from washing machines – must be channelled directly into the sewerage system.

Individual components of greywater systems have a long history. For example, the ordinary water butt, for collecting rain water, is a traditional piece of equipment, and rural communities off the mains water supply already depend on careful water conservation and reuse systems. But official greywater systems are not legal in many countries because of dangers from infectious diseases; existing schemes are generally small-scale and experimental. Several counties in California have legalized greywater systems and the problems of water shortages around Los Angeles have led officials to reconsider the technology. The average Californian produces 400 litres (97 gallons) of reusable greywater per person per day. If just 1% of the population were to reuse their maximum of greywater, the amount of drinking water that would be saved could fill one of the World Trade Centre Buildings to the 50th floor (9.5 billion gallons). With technological advances, greywater recycling offers a practical contribution to cutting our daily waste of such a vital resource. **See also** Compost toilets, Water, pollution of

H

HARDBOARD
Facts
Hardboard is a tough, durable material widely used for woodwork, furniture restoration, and occasionally as a substitute for tropical **timber**. It is manufactured by compressing **wood** fibres together, using high temperatures and pressure. The natural resins within the wood help to bond the fibres; additional resins can be added for extra strength. Hardboard is often treated to make it water- resistant. If you have a choice of hardboards avoid using medium-density fibreboard (MDF). Formaldehyde chemical compounds are used in its manufacture; most European countries have now set exposure limits for this in residential rooms as formaldehyde is suspected of being carcinogenic in high doses, and an irritant to the respiratory system at lower concentrations. MDF is commonly used as a replacement for real wood in panelling, flooring, shop fitting, and furniture. Instead use solid temperate woods or search for low-emission hardboards, which are manufactured without using harmful chemicals.

Reuse/Repair
When buying wood for DIY work or furniture repairs, don't buy tropical hardwoods. If you aren't sure what a wood is, or what it contains, ask before buying. Product labels sometimes give information about the origin of the wood, but mandatory labelling schemes are not compulsory in many countries.

Before buying new hardboards from timber stores find out if a local **salvage** company has supplies. This will not only save money but ensure that wood is reused rather than scrapped or burned. Use leftover pieces for making shelves, bird or bat boxes, or a **compost** container. Give quantities of unwanted wood to refurbishment and repair workshops, not-for-profit organizations, or community groups for reuse.

Use non-toxic varnishes or polishes – hardwoods do require protection from water stains and rot, or give a new lease of life by painting them. **See also** Timber, Wood

HEAVY METALS
Facts
Cadmium, mercury, and lead are just some of the toxic substances found in everyday items such as **paint, dyes, batteries**, and leaded petrol. Mercury and cadmium are particularly dangerous. Human activities and many industrial processes have increased the amount of **heavy metals** circulating in the environment; mining and smelting metal ores, and indiscriminate waste dumping cause particular problems. Industrial effluents contain numerous heavy metals that reach our rivers and seas through the sewerage system.

Within **landfill** sites, heavy metals seep out from corroding **batteries** and other containment **packaging**, and slowly filter through the rest of the infill. If they reach underground water supplies they can contaminate them. In an attempt to keep heavy metals out of household waste many European countries have organized separate collection bins for hazardous items. One German town even issues plastic sacks to its 100,000 residents, asking them to separate out items such as batteries, light bulbs, biro cartridges, and electric cables. Sweden is placing restrictions on certain heavy metals to reduce the overall environmental impact.

Reduce/Reuse/Recycle
One of the most significant actions you can take is to cut down the number of batteries you use. Instead use a transformer and plug equipment into the mains electricity supply. Overall, this saves energy as the manufacture of batteries actually consumes 50 times more energy than they give out during their lifetime.

Items containing heavy metals should be treated with caution. Contact your local authority to see if they offer any special collection services. Don't attempt repairs to highly coloured enamelware – oxides from cadmium and lead are used as pigments in some glazes.
See also Batteries

HIRE, OF EQUIPMENT
Facts
Instead of buying occasionally-used equipment, consider hiring it. Garden centres, specialist stores, and builders' merchants hire out a range of power tools for repair and restoration work, as well as items

such as shredders and chippers for converting organic garden waste materials into a reusable or compostible material.

When choosing **electrical equipment**, reduce energy use by selecting energy-efficient products; information on energy consumption may be available in the accompanying product literature. The product might also bear the energy efficiency sticker, which indicates, with a rating system, the extent to which the product goes beyond the minimum performance limits set by legislation.

Hire equipment should always be in top condition. Before taking equipment home, check its condition and ensure that all electrical fittings are insulated and not worn. Instruction booklets should be given to you. If the equipment is in a potentially dangerous condition, report the matter to the nearest trading standards office.

HOUSEHOLD MATERIALS, HAZARDOUS
Facts
Many common substances are potentially hazardous if they are dumped or poured down the drain. **Paint**, paint stripper, chemical-based floor and oven/stove cleaners, car **batteries**, motor **oil**, filters, anti-freeze, wood preservatives, fungicide treatments, and pesticides all pollute. Quantities of this waste increase every year. In the US the Environmental Hazards Management Institute estimate that in an average city of 100,000 inhabitants, 3.75 tonnes of toilet cleaner, 13.75 tonnes of liquid household cleaners, and 3.44 tonnes of motor oil reach the city's drains every month.

Reduce
It is not always possible to reuse and recycle everything, or to find non-toxic replacements. But you can limit the impact of disposal by buying only the amount you actually need for the task in hand. Better still, reduce the amount of potentially hazardous materials you bring into the home or workplace. Check product labels – items harmful to health are not likely to do the environment much good either. Do you actually need all those different types of household cleaners? And check that products for repair work, especially **adhesives**, are not toxic.

Make sure all potentially dangerous products are clearly labelled, kept in their original container, and are well out of the reach of children. Having bought a product, use it up rather than discarding half-full containers. Perhaps a neighbour could use your left-over paint or car maintenance products? Community groups or charity organizations working on local environmental improvement schemes or housing projects may be able to use up quantities of unwanted paint.

Recycle

Find out if your local service station accepts used motor oil or car batteries for recycling. Some local authorities and waste disposal companies offer special collection points for hazardous materials, or even a travelling "wastemobile" to pick up items for safe disposal. **See** Heavy metals

---

HUMUS

This is the organic material which acts to hold moisture in the soil; lightening heavy clay and providing a better structure, as well as binding light, sandy soils to stop them being blown or washed away. Leafmould makes an excellent humus, so gather autumn leaves and make your own (see **Thrift project**).

Thrift project
How to make leafmould

Make a crumbly soil enricher for your garden/backyard from the yearly leaf fall. Gather the leaves – deciduous ones decay faster than evergreens – and stack them out of the way in a wire mesh frame. Alternatively use plastic dustbin/garbage bin sacks, wetting the leaves first. After a year you should have a coarse mulch that you can dig in to the garden to improve soil structure, or spread it on the soil surface to slow down moisture loss. Leaving the leafmould to rot for another year will produce a finer product.

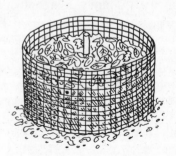

I

INCINERATION
Facts
Getting rid of waste by burning it in incinerators is a controversial issue. High temperatures are needed to destroy complex chemical compounds, including **dioxin**, and **ash** needs to be analyzed prior to **landfill**. Instead of being able to divert materials back into production systems, burning means that potentially reusable materials are destroyed for ever. For example, of the 143,000 tonnes of garbage destroyed at Sydney's Waverley incinerator each year, officials estimate that 75% could have been recycled in one form or another. Because of this, incineration cannot be considered a recycling technique, even if energy recovery takes place. But for some hazardous materials (including medical wastes), incineration remains the safest disposal option.

One advantage is that it does reduce the volume of municipal solid waste by about 90%, making it a favoured option for countries with a shortage of landfill. Switzerland incinerates 80% of its non-recyclable waste, Japan 68%, Sweden 50%, and the Netherlands 50%. Those with advanced recycling programmes usually only burn unrecyclable material, but others use incineration for all waste. Installing pollution control equipment is vital. **See** Bonfires

INSULATION MATERIALS
Facts
Badly insulated buildings waste energy. The Centre for Alternative Technology (UK) estimates that 20% of heating is lost through the roof, 25% through the walls, 10% through the floor, 10% through the windows, and 10% in draughts. Using waste for insulation materials is already taking place; cellulose-based products and shredded paper, treated to make it fire-resistant, are available. Concerns about possible health risks from mineral wool and urea formaldehyde have acted as a catalyst for the development of natural insulation materials.

In Canada, thermal insulation products from recycled **paper** and **wood** have been granted an EcoLogo, the seal of approval from Canada's Environmental Choice programme. And in Australia, shredded **telephone directories** produce a product 25% cheaper than traditional materials. Insulation boards using woodwool, with fibres bound by magnesite – a naturally occurring mineral – have been successfully tested by the Institute of Building Biology in Germany. The boards are free from harmful formaldehyde gas. Insulating boards that are sound-proof, fire-resistant, and made almost entirely from recycled paper are already available in the US.

IRON
Facts

This important ferrous metal is the basic component of **steel**. Wrought iron has been in use for thousands of years, and today cast iron and steel form the backbone of industrial life, with a well-established industry built around its reclamation. Using reclaimed iron gives energy savings of up to 70%. Over half the world's iron comes from Australia and Brazil – metal ores are smelted with coke and limestone.

Reuse

Although iron and steel is collected everywhere for reuse, larger scrap yards tend to be interested only in industrial scrap rather than small household items. But small salvage merchants and street "totters" will accept anything.

Cast iron rusts if it gets wet, so a protective coating of **zinc** is often added to building materials to stop this. Keep your wrought iron garden furniture rust-free with special metal paints; remove rust by sanding down before painting. And give cast-iron **saucepans** a rub with cooking oil after washing. If you cannot reuse or repair items – **tools**, **white goods**, and so on, dismantle them for spare parts – a popular destination for vehicle engines – or give away as scrap.

J

JARS
Facts
Each one of us uses about 100 **bottles** or jars every year; in the UK
8-10% of the contents of the household **dustbin/garbage bin** is **glass**.
Recycling containers makes economic sense. For every tonne of glass
recycled, 135 litres (30 gallons) of **oil** and 1.2 of raw materials are
saved. But reuse is an even better option, extending the life of jars until
they need to be recycled.
Reuse
Jars are ideal for storing nuts and bolts, for mixing **paint** or cleaning
paint brushes, as mini-cloches over seedlings or for keeping slugs off
young plants, or for making a slug trap by sinking them into the soil
and filling with a little beer. Use jar lids for raising flower pots off the
ground to let water drain away. As jars can be made airtight, use them
for storing seeds. Or fill with a little soil and grow plants from fruit pips
(oranges, grapefruit, and lemons germinate fast). In the kitchen, use
jars for storing dried foods bought in bulk, as herb and spice
containers, for bottling home-made jams, chutneys, or fruit, and for
soap scraps and soap solution for handwashing clothes. In the
bathroom keep decorative jars for bathsalts or oils. If you have no use
for jars, give to friends, children's playgroups, local farm produce stalls,
or as a last option, take to a **bottle bank**.

JEWELLERY
Facts
Around the world, scraps of **steel**, **copper**, old **tin cans**, old coins,
beads, feathers, strips of **leather**, and pebbles are fashioned into
decorative ornaments. And jewellery from scrap is becoming
fashionable, the more so as awareness about waste grows. Art and
design students and small businesses are producing commercial items
from old computer components, springs, coils, and metal shavings.
Reuse
Make papier mâché brooches or beads from old **newspapers**; wind the
paper strips around a pencil, allow to dry, then paint and varnish. Use

thin nylon fishing line for restringing beads (see **Thrift project**), and reuse the clips from old brooches. Craft suppliers sell jewellery components and equipment.

Repair
You can repair costume jewellery yourself. If stones in claw mounts are loose, or necklace and bracelet links are coming apart, use a small pair of pliers to secure them. And if a stone falls out, depending on its value, either take it to a jeweller for repair, or replace it with epoxy resin **adhesive**. Roughen the surface of the ring mount first with an emery cloth. Jewellers are able to replace lost precious stones with artificial "paste" stones.

Thrift project
How to rethread a necklace
• Tie a double knot 40mm (1½in) from one end of the new string. Thread on the first bead.
• Butt the bead up to the knot, make a loop and insert the free end of the string. Put a needle through the loop and pull the string to tighten the loop.
• Use a pair of pliers to make sure that the knot is as close to the bead as possible. Add the other beads in the same way.

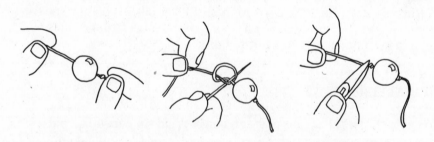

JUMBLE SALES
Facts
Jumble, or rummage, sales are used by many people as a very cheap source of second-hand **clothing**, **fabrics**, kitchen equipment, and general bric-a-brac. Look for details of jumble sales in local newspapers or on library noticeboards.

Reuse
When you are sorting out cupboards at home, keep things for the next jumble sale rather than putting them in the **dustbin/garbage bin**. The most unlikely things sell. Use jumble sales as a cheap source of fabrics for reuse in craftwork or repairs. Take old clothes apart for patchwork (see **Quilts**) or for spare **buttons**, trimmings, or **zips**. Unravel woollen jumpers for reknitting and use feathers from lumpy pillows as cushion or quilt stuffing.

JUNK MAIL
Facts
44% of junk mail is never opened and is immediately thrown away. In the US up to 10% of household waste is junk mail, since advertising in this way is very cheap. It is rarely printed on recycled **paper** and contributes to litter.
Reuse
The best way of avoiding junk mail is to get your name taken off mailing lists by writing to the Mailing Preference Service (see Resources). There is no charge for this service, but it won't stop you from receiving mail from companies whose lists you're already on; so when you get letters from these, send them back unopened with a note on the envelope saying that you do not want to receive any more.

K

KETTLES
Facts
Kettles can waste energy, although energy-efficient appliances that allow you to see how full the kettle is, help cut this loss. Consumer pressure on manufacturers to supply product information about energy consumption, or to implement energy labelling, is essential if more efficient equipment is to be found in high street stores.
Reuse/Repair/Recycle
Refrain from filling the kettle to the brim just for one cup of coffee; heating water is a big energy user. And keep kettles free of "fur" – the build-up of calcium carbonate in hard water areas. Although harmless it reduces the efficiency of equipment; white vinegar left in the kettle overnight will remove it.

If you buy a second-hand kettle, get it checked for safety before use and replace fraying cord. Give unwanted items to electrical refurbishment workshops or charities – stick on a label stating that it is in working condition. Or give to scrap dealers, or street "totters".

KITCHEN UTENSILS
Facts
The most energy-efficient appliances are those powered by your own energy; using manual can openers or carving knives costs you nothing. Choosing the right materials is important too – using **glass** or ceramic baking dishes lowers cooking temperatures by 3.9°C (25°F). Many items are gadgets that are not strictly necessary and are discarded or left to gather dust when they are found to be difficult to clean or maintain. A wide variety of materials is used in utensils – stainless **steel**, **iron**, **aluminium**, **wood**, pottery, **copper**, and **plastics**. Manufacturing or processing these consumes energy and non-renewable resources, and some uses can be inappropriate, for example do not be tempted to buy tropical hardwood chopping boards.
Reuse
Consider whether you really do need items before buying and if you do, choose well-made utensils in durable materials. Do not buy second-

hand items for food preparation that are broken, cracked, or liable to splinter. Even the smallest crack can harbour a variety of bacteria – find another use for china dishes that you repair. They are fine for holding plants, as bonsai trays, or for keeping pens and pencils in. Similarly don't reuse any enamelware that is chipped or cracked, some of the bright colours are based upon pigments that can contain heavy metals such as **cadmium**.

Prolong the life of utensils by careful cleaning and polishing, using natural substances whenever you can. If metal **cutlery** is worn, take it to a metalsmith for replating. And when things are past repair, look for other uses – bent forks and spoons make small gardening tools or paint stirrers, and keep stained or battered **saucepans** for dyeing clothes (see **Dyes**). Give anything you are not using to **charity stores**, **jumble sales**, or to **scrap merchants** or "totters".

KITCHEN WASTE
Facts
The kitchen is one of the main places in the home where waste is generated. Up to 20% (in weight) of the contents of a **dustbin/garbage bin** in the UK, for example, is organic matter – vegetable peelings, food scraps, tea bags, and egg shells. If this is not separated for home composting (see **Compost**), it is likely to be put in the dustbin/garbage bin and eventually end up in a **landfill** site. Here the decaying waste produces a liquid **leachate**,

Vast amounts of **packaging** materials end up in the dustbin/garbage bin, instead of being recycled. A lack of recycling facilities or consumer motivation is not the only reason for such waste. Too much packaging contains a mixture of materials, which are hard to identify and not easily separated. Having identified what is recyclable, another problem is where to put it all. Households served with a kerbside collection scheme are lucky. Rubbish compactors are popular in Germany; wall-mounted **can** crushers effectively flatten cans, allowing five times as many to be stored in the same amount of space. Waste disposal units reduce waste by grinding, but merely add the waste to the sewerage system rather than recycling.
Reuse
We must reduce our waste at source. **Precycling** helps (see p.27).

Avoid buying overpackaged goods and refuse unnecessary bags. Take your own reusable shopping bag with you and keep any plastic carrier bags you do get given. When they split put them in plastic bag recycling containers in supermarkets or recycling centres – they are recycled into garbage bags. Help close the recycling loop by only buying bags made from recycled plastic.

Manufacturing **aluminium** uses tremendous amounts of energy; using foil containers or wrappings once then throwing them away wastes a high-quality metal.

Think innovatively about reusing all the little things – keep **corks**, rubber bands, and yogurt pots. The **plastic** netting used for bundling fruit and vegetables is similar to plastic pot scourers – make your own instead, or refill the bags with stale peanuts and hang from your bird table.

Recycle
If you do not have kerbside collections, find out where your nearest recycling facilities are – collect your **newspapers**, **cans** and **bottles**. Keep a covered bucket in the kitchen for food scraps suitable for the **compost** heap, or dig a compost trench. Advice and equipment is available from organic gardening associations, as well as commercial companies (see Resources). **See** Vermiculture

---

KNITWEAR
Facts
Woollen and synthetic **clothing** makes up a substantial part of all the **rags** and textiles we throw away. Yet they are an important secondary resource, fully recyclable if separated and collected for reprocessing. Manufacturing knitwear is not without its impacts. Processing **wool** uses large amounts of water and chemical treatments; acrylic, the synthetic alternative, is based on petrochemicals and solvents, and even if these are reclaimed and recycled, far more energy is still required to manufacture it. Unlike wool, it is not biodegradable. Metallic dyes, particularly the darker shades, add to the burden of water pollution.

Reuse/Repair/Recycle
Keeping materials in circulation and making fullest use of them is the most appropriate option for recycling. Look out for unbleached "green"

cotton and untreated and undyed wool if you are worried about the impact fabric manufacture has on the environment. Unravel wool for reknitting and do repairs as soon as you notice damage (see **Thrift project**). If you don't have scraps of matching wool, patch with fabric or use **leather** for hardwearing areas such as the elbows on sweaters. Give unwanted knitwear to charity, or recycle through a rag bank. Small pieces make an ideal stuffing for cushions or **toys**.

Thrift project
How to darn
- Make a circle of running stitches around the hole.
- Take the thread back and forth across the hole, keeping them close.
- Weave the thread in and out, keeping the threads close.

KNIVES
Facts
Knives are often ineffective because of a lack of maintenance; a good-quality kitchen or garden knife can last indefinitely. It is better to buy a small set of top-quality knives than keep a drawerful of shoddy, underused equipment. Stainless **steel** doesn't rust and is recyclable.
Reuse
Look on antique stalls and search markets for second-hand **silver** knives – many are very decorative and easily identified by the hallmark. Get damaged knives repaired or replated at silversmiths.

Cutlery knives with scalloped edges have to be reground professionally, but knives with straight edges can be sharpened at home – buy a mechanical sharpening blade in preference to an electrical one. Most knives need to be ground at an angle of 30 degrees. Many hardware stores offer a full professional service for household and garden equipment. Or use a whetstone or carborundum stone for sharpening garden knives.

L

LAMINATES
Facts

Laminates are difficult items for the consumer to reuse or recycle
successfully. **Cartons** are a common example; they are made from
several multi-layered materials that may be bonded together with
adhesives. Paper board, waxed board, polyethylene, and **aluminium
foil** are routinely used. New technologies offer ways of successfully
separating individual components for recycling, but these are still being
developed.

Refuse

In the meantime consumers should question the widespread use of
such laminates in the first place, and instead buy products in alternative
packaging such as recyclable **glass bottles** or **cans**.

LANDFILL
Facts

Approximately 80% of the world's waste ends up in landfill sites. Landfill
is the disposal of waste, usually in existing holes in the ground such as
disused quarries. Some countries dispose of the majority of their **solid
waste** in this way, the UK landfills 90%, others use a combination of
landfill and **incineration** schemes in addition to programmes to divert
recyclable waste into reuse/recycling schemes. For example
Switzerland landfills just 20%, Japan and Denmark 30%, France and
Belgium 35%, and Italy and Germany 65%.

One of the critical factors affecting the future of landfill is the rapidly
dwindling amount of land available in some countries, and spiralling
landfill costs in others. Strategies based on waste reduction are the only
true environmental option for a sustainable future.

Landfill has a permanent presence in the environment. But
decaying organic waste generates explosive **landfill gas** as well as
leachate. Both are potentially hazardous if uncontrolled. Leaking
landfill sites pose a threat to underground water supplies. This risk is
greatest when hazardous materials are disposed of with domestic
waste. The UK remains one of the few countries that persists in this co-

disposal practice, based on the unfounded theory of "dilute and disperse". But some household items, for example **batteries**, also leak **heavy metals**, including **cadmium** and **mercury**, into landfill. This is the prime reason for the special **battery**-collection schemes in parts of Europe and the US. **See also** Landfill gas

LANDFILL GAS
Facts
Decaying organic waste produces methane gas, which combines with carbon dioxide to form explosive landfill gas. Accidents have occurred in residential areas adjacent to old landfill sites. The gas slowly seeps upward through the site, and if badly managed or tapped for reuse as an energy source, it can pose an explosive threat to nearby settlements. Yet if the potential of landfill gas was fully exploited estimates (based on current waste levels) suggest that the energy equivalent of 18 million tonnes of coal a year could be saved. And with better energy conservation and anaerobic digestion technologies this potential could be even bigger – up to 80 million tonnes – enough to satisfy the energy demands of a country the size of Sweden.

In 1990 93% of landfill gas exploitation projects were in the US, Germany, and the UK. More than 240 projects were under way by mid-1991, producing the energy equivalent of more than two million tonnes of coal a year. Worldwide 55% are used for electricity generation, but the gas could be used for heating boilers and kilns, as well as compressing it to form a vehicle fuel.

LEACHATE
Facts
When organic wastes decay within a **landfill**, a liquid, or leachate, is produced. This contains decomposed organic matter and microbes, including disease-causing bacteria. Leachates from modern landfills may also contain known carcinogens and synthetic chemicals; if this liquid leaks into underground water supplies, long-lasting contamination occurs, threatening the purity of drinking water.

Recycle

Keeping hazardous substances out of landfills is a priority. By switching to rechargeable **batteries**, you can prevent some of the most toxic substances from getting into landfills. Programmes for recycling a more comprehensive range of waste materials can help, too. Municipal composting programmes, in some countries, help keep biodegradable materials out of landfill. **See also** Landfill gas

---

LEAD

Facts

Lead is one of the more notorious **heavy metals**. It is poisonous, with no safe level of exposure. The decline of the Roman Empire has been attributed to insanity caused by drinking water from lead plumbing systems. Until such risks were acknowledged, lead was widely used by the building and plumbing industries because of its resistance to corrosion. It is now banned in many countries. Although derived from the mineral ore galena, 60% of the world's supply of lead actually comes from recycled car **batteries**. But in the US, two-thirds of all lead in **landfill** sites is due to car batteries that were dumped instead of recycled. Despite the well-publicized hazards, 90% of the lead in the UK's air comes from vehicle emissions – leaded petrol is still widely available and widely used. Lead is used in metal manufacture and its oxides are used in ceramic glazes, some types of **glass**, and **paint**.

Reduce

Although its use in water supply systems was banned in the UK in 1976, 45% of households are supplied with water that has, at some stage, passed through lead pipes or tanks. Replacing lead pipes is a partial solution, but you can never be totally sure that your water is lead-free, since mains supplies may still be contaminated. Reduce the hazard by running the drinking water tap when it has not been used for a long period – for example, overnight. This will flush out any lead that has dissolved out from the pipes in that time. Water is precious, so run it off into a watering can and use for non-edible plants, or for tasks such as car-washing.

Reuse/Repair/Recycle

Do not reuse lead pipes, or use lead solder in repairs. Avoid paint containing lead. Take care when sanding down or removing old paintwork; wear a face mask to prevent inhaling lead particles. And don't put old wooden or painted items on to bonfires. Be aware of the wider environmental impacts of lead. Use unleaded petrol if your car will run on it – this is essential if you have a catalytic converter. If you fish, use ceramic or plastic weights rather than lead ones. **See** Cadmium

---

LEATHER
Facts
Leather is a specially treated animal skin or hide. Its use goes back to Ancient Egypt and Greece and the tanning industry is a multi-billion dollar enterprise. Between 1983 and 1985 global leather production was approximately 1200 square metres a year.
Refuse
If you don't want to wear or use animal skin, find alternatives made from natural materials, including **rubber**, or synthetics such as **plastic** or **PVC**-coated fabrics. However, be aware that many synthetics are manufactured from a petrochemical base, are not biodegradable, and are energy-intensive to make. The environmental impact from the byproducts and their pollution potential should not be forgotten. Fashion houses are now using alternatives and imitation furs and suedes are very realistic.
Reuse
If properly cared for by regular polishing, leather is extremely hard-wearing and you can patch and mend items such as bags, shoes, clothes, and upholstery. Prolong the life of leather with regular use of natural oils and polishes. Water-proofing agents for suede are only produced as aerosols (see **Aerosol cans**), so choose CFC-free brands. Drying wet suede (pig skin) or leather near a fire weakens it, causing it to crack. Instead, dry slowly and use rolled-up newspaper in shoes to absorb moisture. Keep chamois leathers supple by washing in warm, soapy water and don't rinse out all the soap. Never try to clean or remove stains with dry-cleaning fluid, petrol, or spirit solvents – you will remove the dye. Instead, take items to a professional cleaner.

LEAVES
Facts

Fallen leaves are part of the earth's natural cycle of returning nutrients to the soil. Nothing is wasted. Dead and decaying leaves form leaf mould, rich in minerals, and a useful substitute for peat. Yet each year in our parks and gardens/backyards it is common to see leaves being gathered and burned. Not only do the **bonfires** contribute to air pollution but valuable nutrients are, quite literally, going up in smoke.

Such waste doesn't happen everywhere. In an attempt to keep organic matter out of **landfill** sites and to cut disposal costs, leaf and garden/backyard waste collections are widespread in the US. The material is taken to centralized municipal composting facilities and, after a season or two, the finished **compost** is reused as a soil conditioner back in the parks, or used as a base for landscaping operations. Finished compost is available to the public. Garden/backyard burning is banned in Australia.

Reuse

Reduce your garden/backyard waste by collecting leaves – broad-leaved, deciduous species are best. Add small quantities to your compost heap, or make your own leaf mould (see **Humus**). Leaf mould also makes a good **mulch. See also** Green manure

---

LIGHTING AND LIGHT BULBS
Facts

During its lifetime an ordinary 100-watt, incandescent light bulb uses up to 75 times more electricity than a fluorescent tube or compact bulb. Although energy-efficient bulbs are initially more expensive to buy, the subsequent energy savings will make a significant reduction to your electricity bills. One energy-saving bulb lasts as long as eight ordinary bulbs and uses 80% less electricity. And substituting a compact fluorescent for a traditional bulb keeps half a tonne of carbon dioxide out of the atmosphere over the lifetime of the bulb. 95% of the electricity used in ordinary bulbs is actually given off as heat rather than light. The payback period for an energy-efficient bulb depends on how much it is used, but with moderate use real savings are achieved over a couple of years. The environmental savings in cutting carbon dioxide emissions – an important greenhouse gas – begins immediately.

Lighting uses more electricity than people think. In the US it accounts for 20% of the total electrical output. Yet one billion of the 2.5 billion light sockets could easily use high-efficiency bulbs, giving a potential saving of $30 billion a year. Japan is one of the world leaders in developing more energy-efficient systems.

Reduce

Low-voltage DC lighting gives a bright light with very little drain on your electrical system. Bulbs are available in fluorescent, incandescent, and tungsten halogen form, which are the most efficient form of incandescent lighting, producing a brilliant white light. A 10Wt 12V halogen gives the equivalent light to a 40W 240V domestic lamp. Because of their low wattage, special fittings are not needed.

Switch off all lights when not in use. Start to replace bulbs that are likely to be left on for three hours or more at a time. Long-life incandescents – the tungsten halogen bulbs – give out a softer light than some compact fluorescents. Look for low-energy lighting. For example, desk lamps with 11-watt fluorescent tubes, which provide the lighting equivalent of 75/100 watts. A small but worthwhile point, dust your light bulbs and lighting regularly – dirty bulbs are not energy-efficient.

Lightbulbs cannot be recycled. Compact fluorescents do contain small quantities of **mercury**, but in normal use this should not present any hazards. Unless you have a special collection service for potentially hazardous household substances in your area, old light bulbs will have to go in the **dustbin/garbage bin**. In the US, compact fluorescents and high intensity discharge lighting are being banned from **landfills** and incinerators because of their **mercury** content. Recovery schemes focus on reuse of the mercury and other materials. The fittings for the old-style fluorescent tubes, especially those that have been in place for some years, may contain toxic PCBs. If you are replacing such lighting, seek professional advice on how to deal with the old fittings. Try the environmental health department of your local authority if other sources are not forthcoming.

LINOLEUM (LINO)
Facts
This hard-wearing material is regaining popularity as a floor covering. Natural lino outlasts the synthetic types. It is made from powdered **cork**, linseed oil, wood resins, and wood flour, mixed with fillers such as chalk and clay and fixed on to a jute or hessian backing. Unlike **PVC** flooring, natural lino does not release toxic vapours – volatile organic compounds (VOCs) – and is resilient to scratches and burns. If you look after it well, lino can last for over twenty years.
Reuse
Use scraps or odd sheets of lino as a protective floor covering in kitchens, garages, or outhouses. Make sure the surface to be covered is damp-proofed otherwise the lino backing may rot. Use a piece to cover the top of your **compost** heap – it helps prevent the wind blowing material away and keeps heat in the heap.

Offcuts are ideal for patching small holes in lino. Try to match up patterns and use a non-toxic adhesive. Place a heavy object over the repair to ensure that the surface dries flat.
Recycle
Give unwanted lino to not-for-profit organizations, **jumble sales**, car-boot sales, and, if you have a good quantity, sell it to a **second-hand store**.

LOW-WATER SYSTEMS See Greywater systems

M

MAGAZINES
Facts
Many magazines are printed on glossy paper, which makes recycling difficult. The gloss is achieved by chemical treatments and clay that turns to sludge if recycled. Other potential contaminants include the **adhesives** used for binding, metals such as staples, and inks used in full-colour printing. Many contain undesirable substances that make de-inking processes necessary before recycling. Printing with soy-based inks is more environmentally acceptable.

Magazines that are recyclable produce a low-grade waste, suitable for **packaging** material. Very few newstand journals are printed on recycled paper.

Reduce/Reuse
Cut down on the number of magazines you buy by sharing copies or subscriptions with others. Alternatively read magazines in your local library. Donate copies to doctors' surgeries, hospital waiting rooms, or residential homes for the elderly. Children's playgroups use brightly coloured magazines for craft projects.

Recycle
The low prices paid for mixed waste paper means that many voluntary groups no longer collect magazines for recycling. Check before saving them, but local authorities may accept them in paper banks. Remove all **plastic** wrappings. Keep magazines printed on newsprint for newspaper collections – it helps if you remove the metal staples.

MANURE
Facts
Farmyard manure is rich in plant nutrients and is ideal for improving the soil structure. Huge volumes of livestock slurry are produced daily on farms and in intensive rearing units, so why don't we reuse more of this endless resource? Slurry contains chemicals and antibiotics given to boost growth and inhibit disease and animal wastes are potentially very polluting if they reach rivers and streams. Even when animals are

reared organically, without the use of chemicals, the slurry still contains high levels of nutrients. Recycling manure as a fertilizer ensures that these are reused positively. As a result of legislation, many farms already collect the wastes, either for safe disposal or treatment processes such as anaerobic digestion, using bacteria to break down the waste into less harmful matter. With positive management farm wastes not only produce a high-quality manure but also methane gas, which if tapped is useful for powering equipment and heating buildings.

Reuse/Recycle
You can obtain manure direct from farms and stables, or buy it in a dried and concentrated form. Some types of manure are not suitable for certain plants – check before use. See Resources for stockists of products made from compressed, composted cow manure and duck manure with added straw, as well as liquid organic manure. **Vermiculture** producing worm castings has many small-scale applications, or gardeners can grow special **green manure** plants.

MATTRESSES
Facts
Despite advice from **bedding** manufacturers that mattresses ought to be bought new to ensure total body support, a thriving trade exists for second-hand items. Many people are not aware that some new mattresses contain a proportion of recycled synthetic textiles in the **upholstery**. Discarded **clothing** not suitable for reuse is processed into, among other things, stuffing mixtures. Such a use can affect people with respiratory complaints such as asthma; synthetics slowly release small amounts of vapour from fabric treatments using formaldehyde. This is a known irritant to the respiratory system and you should buy mattresses or futons stuffed with a natural material such as cotton.

Reuse/Recycle
Extend the life of new mattresses by airing and turning them regularly. Remove **plastic** wrappings to allow the mattress to "breathe" and prevent rot. Make or buy a protective fabric cover. If you are buying a second-hand mattress, check that it is firm, not sagging, and that the stuffing is intact. It is not a good idea to patch up loose springs or filling with **foam**.

Recycle

If you want to get rid of a mattress in good condition, contact a local **second-hand store** or charity organization working with the needy and homeless. Try the Salvation Army, Goodwill Industries, or St. Vincent de Paul. Your local social services department is another possibility – they always need household items and may arrange collection. The last option is to take unwanted mattresses to a local civic amenity site for disposal. If you don't have transport, some local authorities operate a free collection scheme for bulky items. Too many mattresses are dumped by the roadside or on waste land – don't add yours to these eyesores. Apart from being antisocial it costs the authorities money to remove it.

MEDICINES
Facts

The pharmaceutical industry uses huge volumes of disposable products and a multiplicity of potentially dangerous substances. While reuse and recycling is not an option for many products, equipment such as sterilization units can produce hygienically clean items, saving resources as well as money. With the potential of being a large polluter, minimizing waste and ensuring safe disposal practices is of paramount importance. Doctors, health care centres, hospitals, dentists, and veterinary practices all produce waste, including radioactive and toxic substances, which require careful disposal.

Studies from the US Environmental Protection Agency (EPA) estimate that 455,000 tonnes of "regulated" medical waste is produced every year in the US. This figure does not include home healthcare wastes, for example the 1.4 billion syringes used by diabetics, kidney dialysis patients, and others. Unfortunately the amount of this type of material ending up in domestic garbage collections is increasing. Discarded drugs and equipment are commonly found at **landfill** sites and rubbish collectors are sometimes injured through careless disposal. **Incineration** is the best option for some clinical wastes. Hospitals are investigating ways of reducing waste, and recycled and unbleached **paper** products are becoming more common.

Reuse/Recycle

At home cut down on the number of chemical products that you use, and return left-over medicine and tablets to doctor's surgeries for safe disposal. Empty medicine bottles are refillable – take them back. Most thermometers contain **mercury**: if they break, take care.

MERCURY
Facts
Mercury, also known as "quicksilver", is familiar as the silvery liquid inside thermometers and barometers. It cannot be recycled and requires careful disposal. Mercury is a poison and is particularly toxic if inhaled. Its use in industry for products such as **batteries**, fungicidal **paints**, and **wood** preservatives means that it can accumulate in the environment, contaminating the food chain.
Reduce/Reuse/Recycle
Spills of mercury in a warm room are a health hazard. If a thermometer breaks, do not allow children to pick up the silver balls. Sweep up as much as possible, wrap in newspaper and preferably dispose of it by taking it to a local pharmacy. Do not use a vacuum cleaner; the mercury can vapourize, making it more dangerous. If a barometer breaks, seek help from your local environmental health department or fire brigade.
See also Heavy metals

METALS see Alloys, Aluminium, Cadmium, Copper, Ferrous metals, Gold, Heavy metals, Iron, Lead, Nickel, Precious metals recovery, Silver, Steel, Tin, Zinc

---

METHANES See Landfill gas

MILL OFFCUTS
Facts
Often termed "mill-broke", this is preconsumer **paper** waste, the scraps and trimmings resulting from manufacturing and printing processes. Paper mills have always fed mill offcuts back into the papermaking process for reuse in the same grade paper, or for **envelope** manufacture. But now mill-broke is commonly marketed as

"recycled" paper; misleading since it does not contain **postconsumer waste** (see p.53).

MIRRORS
Facts
Mirrors are made from silvered glass. Junk stores, **jumble sales**, flea markets, and antique stalls are good places to find old mirrors.
Reuse/Repair/Recycle
Use a mixture of water and white vinegar, damp **newspaper**, or a soft cloth to clean an old mirror. Renovate by stripping and revarnishing wooden frames, or paint. Take chipped or marked glass to a local glass merchant for resilvering. You can use pieces of broken mirror, carefully filed down to reduce sharp edges, for making **mosaics**. In India tiny mirrors are used extensively in embroidery for decorative wall hangings, bags, and cushion covers.

MOSAICS
Facts
The art of mosaic-making dates back into prehistory. In Greece the Byzantine mosaics, made with tiny pieces of marble and other building stone, have attracted worldwide appreciation. In Thailand, the Temple of Dawn is decorated with mosaics of metals and stones, and in modern Barcelona the architecture of Gaudi is adorned with striking mosaics. Different types of mosaics are possible, depending on materials used and location. Environmental art projects breathe life back into desolate urban areas when mosaics are used to decorate walls, playgrounds, and community gardens.
Reuse
Collect weathered coloured **glass** washed up on beaches for making your own mosaics and include sea shells, feathers, pebbles, seeds, broken china, chipped **tiles** (see **Thrift project**, p.249), old internal watch and clock workings, computer parts, and anything else that appeals. Set the pieces into concrete or small picture frames, scrap wood, or strong card. Varnish to add a sheen.

MOTOR OIL see Oil

MULCH
Facts
Mulching is an excellent way of reusing waste materials while improving your garden soil at the same time. Mulching simply means covering the ground with a layer of material such as grass clippings, straw, wood chips, bark shavings, leaves, **paper**, or **cardboard**. This layer protects plants, keeps weeds at bay, and helps retain moisture in the soil; making it an important technique in areas facing water shortages. Some mulches add nutrients to the soil. Black **plastic** is used in agriculture to keep areas weed-free. Unless properly secured this can blow away, adding to the countryside litter problem. Special biodegradable plastics are available, but fragments of disintegrated material are common. In Europe plastic recovery schemes are starting to become established.

MUSICAL INSTRUMENTS
Facts
Many instruments are made from high-quality materials: **wood**, metals including brass, **lead**, and **iron**, and animal skins such as **leather** that continue to have value even when the instrument is past repair. Piano keys, formerly made of ivory, are now made from a substitute, but old keys are still sought after.

Throughout the world many communities make instruments from common, everyday materials, reusing **steel** drums, old **tin** cans, car wheel hub caps, scrap **wood**, coconut shells, and vegetable gourds.
Reuse/Repair
Specialist repair services exist for all types of instruments – ask at a local music store or look in the telephone directory. If you have a valuable instrument to dispose of, try selling it to an antique store or donate to local charitable and community organizations. Scrap merchants take **lead** and brass from old pianos.

N

NAPPIES/DIAPERS
Facts
The disposable nappy/diaper, a potent symbol of our throwaway culture, has aroused passionate debate between manufacturers and environmentalists over its true environmental impact. Consumer attention has forced manufacturers to adopt safer methods of bleaching the pulp padding; chlorine bleaching left small traces of **dioxin**, one of the most poisonous substances known to humankind. But questions remain unanswered about the potential pollution problem of disposing of untreated human waste in **landfill** sites.

About 4% of the UK's domestic waste is disposable nappies/diapers. Over 3.5 billion are thrown away every year – most ending up in landfill. Despite a trend back to the reusable cotton nappy/diaper and the availability of washing services, sales of disposables continue to soar. In the US nappies/diapers are being promoted as recyclable, but there are no large-scale recycling schemes. In an attempt to make disposables appear more "environmentally friendly", a leading brand name is running a trial composting programme. The **plastic** linings complicate this, but there are plans to recycle these into flower pots and rubbish bags. The pulp padding is used for making **cardboard** and insulation materials.

Fuelling the debate, research from a US environmental group, published in 1991, argues that disposables create more than seven times as much postconsumer waste as reusables, and during manufacture produce three times as much waste. Disposables also use 37% more water than laundered reusables. The debate over energy savings is less clear. Nappy/diaper washing services can save more energy than individuals can washing at home, but their transportation adds to pollution and energy use. A leading brand of nappies/diapers concluded that "when all factors are considered neither cloth nor disposable nappies have an overall significant advantage for the environment".

Reduce/Reuse/Recycle
If you opt for disposables think about alternating them with reusables to cut waste, or buy reusable covers that only need a liner. Give

unwanted cloth nappies/diapers to **charity stores** or **jumble sales**. Use worn-out ones as cleaning and dusting cloths, or as wiping cloths for car maintenance.

NEWSPAPERS
Facts
Every day around the world, millions of newspapers are discarded. In the US over 62 million newspapers are printed each day, using 23,000 tonnes of newsprint. According to the American Paper Institute, the average American consumes about the equivalent to one tree per person of newsprint annually.

Even though newsprint is a renewable resource – manufactured from **wood pulp** or from varying amounts of waste paper – it does not make environmental sense to use virgin pulp for these short-lived products. Worldwide, far more newsprint could contain a greater percentage of recycled material. A survey by Friends of the Earth UK in 1990 revealed just how little waste paper is currently being used. None of the newspapers could provide an annual average for the minimum amount of recycled fibre they use, and overall the highest percentage was only 39%. Governments should develop markets for secondary materials by setting mandatory quotas for recycled materials. In the UK the Advisory Committee on Business and the Environment (ACBE) is calling for a requirement for newspapers to use an average of at least 35% de-inked recycled fibre within two years. In the US publishers in New York have committed themselves to increasing the amount of recycled fibre from a tiny 7% in 1989 to 40% by the year 2000. Newspapers could use up to 60% without changing the existing equipment. 100% recycled newsprint is now available.

For an industry with huge fuel bills the benefits of recycling include large energy savings. Manufacturing newsprint from waste paper uses between 25 and 60% less energy than newsprint derived from new **wood pulp**. Air pollution is cut by up to 74% and water pollution is reduced by 34%. Industry is investigating alternative commercial uses for waste newsprint including: animal bedding, a non-polluting wall board, and insulation material.

Small amounts of newspapers can be composted with other materials (see **Compost**) although the ink content has raised concern;

most are based on petroleum-derived solvents or oils, and even the
soybean oil subsitutes can contain pigments derived from **heavy
metals** and chemical hydrocarbons. Pressure in the US from the
American Newspaper Publishers Association has meant that 50% of the
newspapers printed in the US now use "soy-based" inks. Since little is
known about what happens to these toxic components of ink in the soil,
the safest advice is only to use newspapers in compost where it is not
being used for food-growing.

Reduce/Reuse

Every home or workplace faces the problem of what to do with all those
newspapers, especially if there are no collecting schemes near by.
Consider ways of cutting down the amount of newspaper. Why not get
your household into the habit of only buying one newspaper a day, and
leave those you've read in a communal workplace area, canteen, or
coffee room.

Small amounts of newspaper are easily reused around the home – for
animal bedding, lining bird cages or the **dustbin**, putting underneath
carpets as an extra layer of insulation, and as a protective layer when
painting or decorating. If you are changing car **oil** or doing
maintenance work, use sheets of newspaper as a replaceable covering
for garage floors or concrete areas. Damp newspaper makes a good
window polisher and newspaper logs or "brickettes" can be made for
open fires with special equipment, or make simple firelighters by
rolling sheets together.

In the garden/backyard add small amounts of newspaper to the
compost heap and dig it in to compost trenches. Shredding it first will
help speed its breakdown. Try making flower pots for seedlings from
newspaper. Use yogurt pots as a mould for papier mâché, or buy a
special kit. As the seedlings grow their roots penetrate the
biodegradable paper, making it easy to plant the whole pot out,
reducing possible damage to seedlings.

Recycle

Newspaper collection schemes are always the hardest hit in the
fluctuating paper market. Whenever there is a glut of low-grade paper,
many collections, particularly volunteer schemes collecting paper for
community or charity projects, find it is no longer financially viable to
continue collecting. At such times paper merchants are generally only
interested in the higher grades of paper – white office waste and

computer paper. So before you start collecting, check that there is a local outlet, either through door-to-door charity collections, local authority kerbside collections, or paper banks at recycling centres or outside supermarket stores. Information on local collections is often publicized in community newspapers, on library notice boards, or contact your local authority or environmental group.

Within the home separate newspapers from the rest of your waste. If possible, set aside a special box or place where you can stack them – they will usually need tying or bundling for door-to-door collections. Use biodegradable string rather than old tights/pantyhose. Don't include colour magazines – they are made from a different grade of paper, often chemically treated, which will hinder the recycling process. Ask your collector what is and what is not acceptable.

NICKEL
Facts
Nickel is a metal commonly found in nickel-cadmium **batteries**. The world's reserves are estimated at one million tonnes, but substantial amounts are known to exist in manganese nodules on the ocean seabed. Recovering nickel for reuse from exhausted rechargeable batteries is possible, but rates have generally been low. But now a promising pilot scheme in the Netherlands is managing to recover 60% nickel as a pure metal, as well as 99% of the cadmium. This is a great help in cutting the environmental impact of disposing of such batteries when exhausted or no longer rechargeable.
Reuse/Recycle
You should regard batteries as household hazardous waste. Special collections for safe disposal exist in many environmentally aware countries, including Switzerland, Italy, Germany, and Denmark. In Seattle, USA, a touring "wastemobile" collects them. Find out what facilities exist in your area. Put pressure on your local authority for such facilities at recycling centres or civic amenity sites.

NIGHTSOIL
Facts
This is the polite term for human excrement, which is collected for reuse in many parts of Asia. Around the large cities in Japan, South Korea, and China there are vegetable-growing greenbelts that rely on such waste. It is either applied directly to the soil after having been left to mature (thus ridding it of any disease-carrying organisms or bacteria) or treated sewage water is pumped directly on to the fields. Shanghai actually produces an exportable surplus of vegetables. And in India nightsoil is the basic component of Calcutta's aquaculture system, producing 20,000kg (44,080lb) of high-protein fish for sale every day. In Yemen the whole economy was based on recyclable materials until the 1960s. Nothing was wasted, products were re-utilized or remanufactured, and human excrement was dried, collected, and used as fuel in public bathhouses. In turn, the ashes were sold to gardeners as a fertilizer.

Reusing nightsoil productively follows the pattern of nature; organic matter is recycled by other organisms, returning nutrients to the soil. Small-scale domestic reuse is also possible with **compost** and waterless toilets, and the practice of spreading sewage sludge on agricultural land as a fertilizer is common – although some curbs are now being introduced as the sewage from industrialized areas may contain toxic **heavy metals**. Alternative ways of treating it, such as reed-bed technology, are becoming popular.
Reuse
If you live in a rural location, you may want to consider installing alternatives to cesspits or septic tanks. A range of compost or waterless toilets is available (see Resources). However do not attempt large-scale recycling before seeking guidance on avoiding health and pollution hazards. Manufacturers are one source of help, or contact your local environmental health department.

OFFICE EQUIPMENT
Facts
Every day offices and workplaces generate large quantities of materials that are usually eventually thrown away. Yet **paper**, **cardboard**, **plastics**, and textiles are all recyclable and most metals are in demand by scrap and **salvage** merchants. Production waste – the material that never reaches the consumer – is easy to reuse as it is generally uncontaminated with other materials. Office refurbishment schemes add to the burden of waste – good-quality furniture, **carpets**, and floor coverings frequently end up in rubbish skips/dumpsters, along with unwanted **telephones**, **typewriters**, filing cabinets, and outdated office stationery. Inefficient use of equipment in the US is estimated to cost businesses billions worth of electricity every year. Use the energy-saving switch on photocopiers – they give savings of up to 90% – and switch equipment off when not in use.

Reduce/Reuse/Recycle
Packaging materials account for a high proportion of such waste. Could cardboard and plastic wrappings be returned to suppliers for reuse? Or could they be reused in the office? If your company uses packing products are they paper-based or recyclable? If not, why not? Try switching to alternatives to **polystyrene** packaging chips such as shredded paper, **wood** shavings, or recycled paper pulp. Or keep chips and reuse them, and put a note in the package asking the recipient to do the same.

   Cut waste and save money by getting typewriter (see **Typewriters**) and computer printer ribbon re-inked and photocopier toner cartridges refilled. Rethink all office practices to reduce waste at source. Obsolete equipment may still be in working order – many charities depend on donations of office equipment and furnishings to keep their overheads down. If you return items such as telephones or broken computers to manufacturers, components and precious metals can be separated and recovered for reuse.

   Start a workplace recycling scheme or participate in local collections of office paper.

OFFICE WASTEPAPER
Facts
Many office practices are very wasteful. Single-sided documents are discarded after reading, and rather than circulating one or two copies, each person has their own – often to be read only once then thrown away. Huge amounts of valuable computer paper and rejected photocopies end up in the **dustbin/garbage bin**.

Why do we throw away this high-grade **paper**, which is always in demand as a pulp substitute? According to one estimate, more than 350 million trees are cut down every year to make office paper. Yet vast amounts are lost from the recycling system. In the UK 130,000 tonnes of office paper are lost every year. By not recycling paper we are creating unnecessary pressures on existing forests, as well as increasing the amount of forest land specifically planted for paper. Such plantations are unbalanced ecosystems, usually containing only one or two tree species, and dependent on large quantities of pesticides.

In the UK, the Independent Waste Paper Processors Association promotes an innovative initiative designed to close the recycling loop. Waste paper from offices is collected and sold for repulping and conversion into washroom and wiping products. These 100% recycled products are, in turn, sold back to participating companies, thus completing the recycling loop.
Reduce/Reuse
Reduce waste by appropriate use of office paper. Keep unwanted documents in a special box and use it as scrap paper. Or take old reports apart, staple the unused sides together and make notepads. Old computer paper is ideal for rough drafts or for children's projects.
Recycle
If paper cannot be reused because it is already printed on both sides, start a recycling pile. White office paper and computer listings fetch the best prices – check with collectors about the minimum quantities accepted and types of paper. Seek advice on what can and cannot be recycled. For example, some fax paper has a thermal coating that hinders recycling. And just as important as collecting paper is actually buying recycled paper. This helps to create a bigger demand for it, which in turn helps to bring the price down, increasing its availability and helping to ensure that there is an adequate market for collected waste paper.

OIL
Facts
Waste lubricating oil from vehicles is recyclable, yet every year millions of litres are dumped or poured down the drain. This practice is not only wasteful but also potentially dangerous. Waste oil contains toxic substances that are polluting if not dealt with properly. Just four litres of oil (the amount from one car oil change) will contaminate an area of water twice the size of a football pitch/soccer field. And if the oil reaches a sewage works through the drainage system, it can kill the bacteria needed for effective sewage treatment.

Reclaiming motor oil for reuse saves precious petroleum and energy resources. According to the US Association of Petroleum Re-refiners "oil never wears out, it just gets dirty". Re-refined lubricating oil has been proved to be equal in quality and performance to that made from virgin oils and yet so little is recovered. Some is re-refined back into motor oil or a high-quality lubricant, while the rest goes into manufacturing fuel oil for industrial boilers. Italy has an impressive recycling rate – collection schemes are expected to recover 83% of waste oil in 1991. Elsewhere industry-backed schemes are being set up in a welcome initiative.

It is actually illegal to dump waste oil down the drain in many countries, including the UK and US, yet estimates show that the amount of oil used in vehicle DIY oil changes is equal to the amount dumped each year. In the US this loss could power 360,000 homes for one year if it was collected for recycling. The annual amount dumped on the ground, down kerbside drains, and in rubbish is 11 times the amount lost in the Exxon Valdez tanker spill. In some places appropriate symbols are painted on drains as a reminder not to dump. Seattle, USA, uses a fish accompanied by a warning that oil kills.

Reduce/Reuse/Recycle
If you are changing your car oil, only buy what you actually need. Check in advance whether a local service station or garage accepts oil back for recycling. If not they should be able to recommend somewhere else. The Chemical Recovery Association in the UK (and similar bodies in other countries) operates a network of collection points, and civic amenity sites and recycling centres usually have such facilities. Whatever you do, do not dump oil.

ORGANIC WASTE
Facts
The volume of organic waste produced globally increases every year. As well as all the **paper** and **cardboard** nearly 30% of household rubbish is organic material – such as vegetable and fruit peelings, uneaten food, and garden refuse. Unless recycled at source, for example by composting, all this ends up in **landfill** sites, where it is potentially the most polluting percentage of the fill. Bacteria and microorganisms attack the mixed waste, breaking down the organic matter to form a liquid (**leachate**), which leaches into the ground. This leachate contains partly rotten matter, bacteria, and byproducts of decomposition, and may be contaminated by chemicals present in the landfill. If it leaks out into groundwater supplies, it creates a serious hazard. The decaying organic waste also produces methane, a powerful greenhouse gas.

By composting your organic wastes you can alleviate pressure on landfill sites, and enrich your garden/backyard. Larger composting schemes can yield a valuable soil conditioner. Such schemes, including composting, along with other materials, are gaining popularity.

But vegetable refuse is not the only organic waste. Every day millions of litres of human sewage and animal wastes have to be treated for safe disposal. Dumping sewage sludge at sea is no longer tolerated by most countries. **Incineration**, the alternative favoured by some, can cause air pollution and destroys a potentially valuable resource. New uses for this nutrient-rich material are being tried. Sewage sludge already provides fertilizer for agricultural land; but it has to be strictly monitored to ensure that levels of **heavy metals**, introduced by industrial effluent, do not build up within the soil. Various sludge-drying techniques are being developed, and reed-bed processing (see **Reed bed systems**) of sewage is a new and promising technology.

Reduce
Examine the organic waste you throw away. Could you reduce it in volume? Certain fruit and vegetables, for example, do not need peeling if washed properly. By eating the peel you obtain the nutrients and vitamins often found there. The argument that you must peel because of pesticides used in farming does not hold up since pesticides can penetrate deep inside fruit and vegetables, so you should buy organic produce or grow your own.

Reuse
For inedible kitchen wastes, keep a separate bucket in the kitchen. If you have a garden, build a **compost** heap or buy a compost tumbler (see **Tumbler, compost**). If not, donate the waste to someone who does have a compost system, or ask your local authority to start a community composting scheme. Kerbside collection schemes often collect organic wastes separately. Compost your garden/backyard wastes too, or use as **mulch**. Don't put leaves on **bonfires**, instead make your own leafmould (see **Humus**). Leaf collection and yardwaste schemes are common alternatives in the US and Canada. As a last resort take any waste you cannot deal with to a civic amenity site. **See also** Landfill gas, Shredders

P

PACKAGING
Facts

One-third of domestic rubbish is packaging. (PIRA) **glass, aluminium, steel,** laminated **cartons, paper,** and **cardboard** are other popular packaging materials with varying rates of reuse and recycling, often dependent on manufacture-led recovery programmes, or legislative controls. Negotiating the EC Packaging Directive has proved highly contentious; although the aims are laudable, reducing the amount of packaging at source, cutting back on the amounts ending up in **landfill** and drastically increasing recycling programmes, the packaging industry has fought hard to keep options open. The proposed Directive obliges member states to 1) Achieve a 90% recovery of packaging waste within 10 years of the Directive being passed, with at least 60% of packaging waste being recycled. 2) Take packaging waste out of the general waste stream within 10 years, only the residues of the collection and sorting process (to a maximum of 10% by weight) can be disposed of in landfill or by incineration. 3) Prepare national waste management plans stating when they will achieve interim thresholds of 60% recovery at 40% recycling.

In Germany the Duales system sets tough targets for reducing packaging waste, although it has been criticized by the European packaging lobby for evading EC controls and restricting trade. It has also been called highly irresponsible as collection rates outpace existing markers for secondary materials. As a result huge volumes are being offered outside Germany at cut-price rates, and even free of charge, to companies and processors elsewhere in Europe, and beyond. The plastics industry is particularly hard hit by these cheap supplies, which in the UK are undermining the many pilot recycling schemes.

Tackling the packaging problem is a huge issue; the industry is surrounded by vested interests, inaccurate claims, and over-simplified statements when comparing product's resources and energy consumptions. But a backlash is now under way. In the US the Environmental Protection Agency is beginning to set standards regulating the use of statements about recyclability. And elsewhere credence should be given to those manufacturers who are setting up pilot recycling programmes, or amending the wording on their products to avoid misleading the consumer. The use of economic instruments, such as packaging levies, are alternative incentives to get manufacturers to close the recycling loop.

Reduce/Reuse/Recycle
Using no packaging should be the ultimate goal, otherwise keep it to a minimum. Avoid single use, disposable items; those that are hard to recycle locally and packaging that definitely cannot easily be recycled. Recycled paper products are not hard to find, returnable glass is a little more difficult in many countries. **See also** PET, Polystyrene, Polythene, Wood pulp

---

PAINT
Facts
Household paints are among the most common household hazardous materials. Because of their organic solvent content some countries operate special collections to keep paint out of municipal waste. In California householders are only allowed to dispose of completely dry latex paint in their **dustbins/garbage bins**, the rest, including paint thinners, has to be put into hazardous waste containers.

The hazard arises from organic solvents that evaporate to form ozone and other pollutants. Metallic-based paints used by the vehicle industry release up to 15 litres (3 gallons) of solvent for every car. Paints may also contain other chemicals that include fungicides, and despite its toxic effects **lead** is still to be found in some paints. But environmental pressure has forced manufacturers to reduce solvent use by developing water-based paints.

Reuse
Read the labels carefully before buying – the more responsible manufacturers list all the ingredients. Latex paints are free from flammable and toxic solvents, and paints based entirely on plant extracts and natural oils are becoming more widely available. Reduce waste by buying only what you need, and then use it all or give the remainder away. Not-for-profit groups may be able to use leftover paint for community projects or environmental improvements.

Recycle
Find out if your local authority operates any special collections. Don't

put paint cans or old painted **wood** on **bonfires** – burning can cause pollution or release lead.

PAPER
Facts
Paper consumption is often used as an indicator of wealth. In the US the current per capita consumption is 311kg (666lb) per year, compared with 163kg (360lb) in the UK, dropping to 26kg (571lb) in Brazil, 15kg (33lb) in Thailand, and less than 1kg (2lb) for over half the African nations. Yet among the bigger users, paper is often wasted or used inappropriately. Recycling rates in industrialized countries are increasing, but much waste paper is recycled into relatively low-grade **packaging** or **cardboard**. Of the 550–650,000 tonnes of newsprint used in Australia each year, only 37% is recycled. In the US "recycled content" targets and operating procurement policies are being set that favour recycled products.

Increasing recycling is desirable on environmental and economic grounds. Paper is a renewable resource and biodegradable. But it makes little sense to **landfill** it as disposal costs rise and when countries such as the UK import two-thirds of their paper needs.

Cutting consumption and increasing recycling would substantially help cut the impact of papermaking on the environment. Processing and bleaching virgin **wood pulp** releases toxic chemicals, yet recycling cuts air pollution by 74% and water pollution by 34%. Demand for more paper leads to irreplaceable habitats being destroyed. In Canada, the old-growth forests in British Columbia are under threat from the chain saw and in Sweden former forests of mixed broadleaved trees have been replaced by conifer plantations. This type of forestry does not support a variety of wildlife; the soil slowly becomes acidic and is eventually less productive.
Reuse/Recycle
Consider ways of reducing your paper use. Simple things such as using the backs of old **envelopes** and reports for scrap paper is a start. Reuse envelopes by buying special **adhesive** reuse labels. Use both sides of writing or photocopying paper. Within the home cut the use of unnecessary paper products; use **rags** for cleaning rather than disposable paper towels, and when you do buy paper, choose recycled

and non-chlorine-bleached. Use fabric table napkins instead of paper ones, save old **newspapers**, white office paper, and computer paper for kerbside and other paper collections. Keep office stationery paper separate from the rest – its quality makes it suitable as a direct substitute for pulp in papermaking. Paper collectors pay more for this material. Cut down on packaging materials – when you shop, precycle by avoiding excessively packaged items. Instead buy loose or minimally wrapped items in recyclable paper. Save wrapping paper to use again (iron if necessary) and recycle greetings cards by pasting them on to folded, coloured paper or cutting them down to make gift tags. **See also** Toilet paper, Unbleached products, Waste paper

---

PATCHWORK see Quilts

PET (Polyethylene terephthalate)
Facts
PET is a high-quality **plastic**. In Europe approximately 450 tonnes are used each year and of this 285 million tonnes are used in packaging. The majority is recyclable if it is recovered separately from the rest of the waste. Because PET is such a high-performance plastic the industry is keen to develop extensive recycling schemes; legislation promoting recyclables remains another underlying pressure on the packaging industry. Manufacturing PET is energy-intensive, producing substantial amounts of hydrocarbons. Yet PET is lightweight, so transporting PET **bottles** saves up to 40% of energy costs if compared with transporting **glass** ones. Bottle bills (legislation) in the US have made PET the most recycled plastic – one out of every four PET bottles is reclaimed for recycling.

In Switzerland a pilot scheme for returnable, refillable bottles was such a success that other countries, including Germany and the Netherlands, are now using them. The bottles are laser-marked at the refilling stage, and after 26 trips are sent for recycling. A PET bottle made with 25% recycled PET is now on supermarket shelves in the US – this is believed to be the first time recycled PET has been used in direct contact with food. And a major drinks company is starting to use them in the UK.

Europe's first full-scale PET recovery plant opened in the Netherlands in 1990. Clean PET flake is then shipped to Ireland for conversion into polyester fibre for **carpets**, textiles, and for fibrefill for **clothing** and duvets. Just five recycled PET bottles makes enough fibrefill to stuff a ski jacket. Reclaimed PET is also used for **car** components and the base caps for PET bottles.

Reuse

If you don't have recycling banks for plastic bottles, consider buying items in refillable or recyclable glass. If the bottle has a deposit on it, always return it. You can use discarded bottles to make a number of useful items (see **Thrift project**).

Recycle

Some plastic collection schemes may accept PET containers only. If the container is not labelled or coded it is difficult to distinguish clear PET bottles from clear **PVC**. Generally a PVC bottle has a seam running lengthways while a PET bottle does not. Give bottles a rinse in leftover washing-up water before putting in **bottle banks** or out for kerbside collections. Some collectors will want you to flatten the bottle first to take up less room (to save energy), but countries with bottle bills will not redeem the bottles if they have been flattened.

Thrift projects

Ideas for PET bottles

- Cut empty plastic bottles in half to make mini cloches for raising seeds.
- Cut the neck off a bottle to make a plastic funnel.
- Fill bottles with water to make a solar water heater.

PHOTOGRAPHY EQUIPMENT AND FILMS see Cameras, Silver

PLASTIC
Facts
Plastic accounts for 7% by weight of household waste, and occupies about 20-30% of **dustbins/trash cans** in industrialized nations. Worldwide over 100 million tonnes of plastic are produced every year. The basic raw material is petroleum oil, a non-renewable resource. While factory scrap is routinely fed back in to the production process, the recycling of postconsumer plastic is still very much in its infancy.

Over 50 different types of plastic (polymers) exist, but even the most used have relatively low recycling rates. In the European Community between 7 and 8% of plastic is recycled; over 11.5 million tonnes of easily recoverable plastic is thrown away every year – with the average family discarding 40kg (88lb) annually. The UK's recycling rate is even lower, just 4%. Plastics production in 1990 was 2.2 million tonnes, consumption was 3.5 million tonnes. Plastics packaging accounted for over 1.2 million tonnes. Most was used in products with a lifetime of less than one year. Some polymers, such as polypropylene, do produce a high-grade product if they are recycled. However, in the US over 3.5 million tonnes a year are used and only 1% is recycled. A lack of information about available secondary markets for reclaimed plastics is one of the most severe handicaps facing the industry.

Recycling rates will undoubtedly improve as tougher legislation prevents recyclable material from ending up in **landfill** sites. Most countries are devising waste minimization plans – it is hoped that these will encourage local authorities to work with the plastics industry to set up more plastic collection schemes and put pressure on designers to use mixed materials more responsibly. While life without plastics is difficult to imagine, certain uses do little to ease the growing volumes of rubbish.

Identifying different types of plastic is difficult unless **bottles** or other items are marked. The numbering coding system used in the US was devised by the plastics industry.

Consumption of **PVC** and **polystyrene** is enormous, but fears of toxic substances from burning PVC and the former use of CFCs in polystyrene has led manufacturers to switch to substitute **paper** or paperboard packaging. But the use of plastics need not be detrimental to the environment. With careful product design plastic can actually lead to energy and resource savings when compared with other materials. A German study in 1987 reported that without plastic the weight of household packaging waste would increase by a factor of 400; energy use would go up by 200%; and the volume of waste needing disposal would rise by 256%. Since plastic is also a light material, savings are made in transportation costs of finished products.

However all materials have some impact on the environment and the one major drawback to plastic is its petrochemical base and its inability to biodegrade. Degradable plastics that break down under certain conditions are the subject of much controversy. Even the newer formulations, made from the fermentation of sugars rather than mineral oil, have not escaped criticism. From the environmental viewpoint it is far better to reuse a product by refilling or reclaiming it for recycling than to use degradable plastic. The only exceptions are certain "niche" areas – plastic as an agricultural **mulch**, certain maritime uses, and rubbish bags from recycled plastic waste. 90% of branded garbage bags in the US were degradable by the end of 1989.

Plastic waste does not have to be manufactured into the same product. Mixed plastics can be fabricated into a material that resembles wood, yet is rot-proof, or into products such as motorway markers, posts, and fences. The value of such a process is that it extends the life of the plastic waste and replaces the use of virgin materials.

Plastic has a high calorific value, around 38 megajoules per kilogram (MJ/kg). This makes it suitable for energy from waste schemes. Although, strictly speaking, this is not recycling, it captures heat for reuse. Examples of remanufactured products using plastic waste include: garden furniture, plastic **wood**, industrial textiles, garbage bags, **bottles**, **carpets**, and as a filling for **clothing** and cushions.

Reuse

Cut down on the amount of plastic **packaging** you buy, especially if there are no established plastic collection schemes in your area. Avoid buying pre-packaged fruit and vegetables. Wash and reuse containers for storing food, but do not reuse anything that once contained chemicals or mineral oil. Refill containers – either buy in bulk or take the container back to the store for refilling. Where bottle deposits exist, return all bottles to stores or "buy back" centres.

Repair/Recycle
Specialist polymers include nylon and polyester. While these are hard-wearing materials, they are synthetic fibres, so certain types of **adhesive** should not be used on them or the fibres will melt, and do not use an iron or chemical cleaning products. Read garment labels and if in doubt have items cleaned professionally. Check the label or coding system on container bases. Not all recycling centres or kerbside collection schemes accept all types of plastic. **See also** Cartons, Laminates

---

PLASTIC BAGS
Facts
Using a plastic bag to carry shopping home and then throwing it in the **dustbin/garbage bin** is extremely wasteful. Too much plastic ends up in **landfill** or **incineration** after a very short life. Globally we are using more plastic bags every year. In Canada the average family uses 13 shopping bags every week – in 1989 this totalled over three billion plastic bags and 53 million kraft paper bags. Unfortunately research reveals that most were discarded after use. In the UK one leading supermarket chain estimates that its customers use ten million plastic carrier bags every week, and that a 10% reduction would be possible if people reused them. Such action would save over 1000 tonnes of plastic and the equivalent of more than one million gallons of **oil** a year.

The response from industry is to produce stronger bags that can be reused, and to manufacture bags and rubbish sacks made from reclaimed waste plastic. Fierce debate surrounds the most appropriate choice of material for bags. The Canadian plastics industry claims that a paper bag consumes more than five times the energy needed to produce a plastic bag and in a **landfill** the paper bag occupies ten times more space than plastic. The British Plastics Federation claims that plastic bags weigh one-sixth the weight of a paper bag.

The Environment and Plastics Institute of Canada argues that paper mills produce between 80 and 230kg (176–507lb) of sulphur emissions per tonne of paper, while plastics manufacture releases just 17kg (37lb) per tonne. However, such comparisons are meaningless unless the whole environmental impact of a product is taken into account – the eco-balance or "cradle to grave" approach.

The use of biodegradable plastics is now known not to offer any significant reductions in the environmental impact of disposing of waste plastic packaging. This has led to a shift back to easily identifiable low-density **polythene** and to reusable non-chlorine-bleached cotton bags.

Reuse/Recycle

Precycle by avoiding using plastic bags wherever possible. Take a durable shopping bag with you and try to buy goods loose. If you have carrier bags, reuse them for another shopping trip. Donate those you cannot use to market stall traders, **jumble sales**, or **second-hand stores**. Save torn plastic bags for plastic collection banks in supermarkets. If it says LDPE or recyclable on the bag, they can be recycled. **Cellophane** bags, made from **wood** fibre, and plastic wrappings lined with **aluminium** foil cannot be recycled.

PLASTIC WRAPPING

Facts

Plastic wrapping is everywhere. In the US plastic wrappings, including bags, make up 40% of all plastic rubbish. With around five million tonnes in use each year, the recycling rate is extremely small. In the UK polythene film is the most widely used and recycled type of plastic wrapping, with over 50,000 tonnes recovered each year. But this only represents 10% of total UK production, so persuading more large users, and particularly retailers, to separate pallet wrappings, bags, and sacks for recycling is an important target. Recovering household plastic waste is much more problematic. Plastic film makes up 5.5% of domestic waste. Manufacturers are investigating ways of labelling it to allow a greater recycling rate.

Reuse

Cutting down on plastic waste must always be the first option. Buy unwrapped vegetables and fruit, and choose other foods in simple, single-material packaging. Avoid the need for shopping bags by taking your own. Plastic bags are easy to reuse – wash them if necessary. Shrink-wrapping (see **Clingfilm/plastic wrap**) is more problematic.

PLYWOOD

Facts

Plywood is manufactured from **wood** sheets or **timber** veneers bonded together with synthetic resin adhesives. Plywood is hard-wearing and popular for doors, furniture, and repair work. Finland is currently the world's largest manufacturer of plywood, supplying a range of temperate hardwood veneers. Unfortunately demand for tropical hardwoods remains high, and the UK is one of the world's largest consumers of tropical hardwoods, including large quantities of plywood. Indonesia supplies approximately half of the UK's imports of tropical plywood. But while these products contribute more revenue to the exporting country than logs, the environmental price is high. The wood-processing factories are often inefficient, leading to unnecessary felling and pollution.

Reuse

If you are buying plywood items check that they are not made from tropical timbers. Temperate alternatives include alder, ash, beech, oak, and douglas fir. As an alternative to plywood use imitation wood products made from mixed **plastic** waste. These can be sawn, hammered, and nailed without splitting, and they don't rot.

A growing number of timber merchants stock salvaged wood from **demolition sites** and building restorations. Take unwanted **wood** to furniture repair workshops or find out if a local environmental or community group can use it. Alternatively leave it in a street skip/ dumpster – it will disappear quickly, or dispose of it at your local civic amenity site.

Repair

For outdoor use, plywoods based on pine or other softwoods need treating with wood preservatives, **paint**, or similar products if they are to last. Many products are toxic and classified as household hazardous waste for disposal purposes – look for the least toxic.

Salvage or wood yards may have stocks of wood suitable for repair work. Damaged furniture, particularly the backs of cabinets, can be restored with new plywood. Many temperate hardwood veneers are resistant to knocks and scratches, but damaged wood surfaces are repairable with proprietary wood fillers and scratch removers. **See also** Hardboard

POLYSTYRENE
Facts
Polystyrene foam containers for fast food, cups from vending machines and packaging "chips" for fragile objects frequently end up as rubbish or litter. As well as being targets for the environmental lobby due to the former use of CFCs and now their related compounds for foam blowing, they have become a potent symbol of our throwaway society.

Over one-third of polystyrene in the US is used for **packaging**. Officials in Berkeley, California, and Portland, Oregon, have passed legislation banning polystyrene containers. Every year Americans use over 25 billion polystyrene foam cups. But now many workplaces and food establishments operate collecting schemes, funded by the **plastics** industry. Polystyrene can be washed, ground into pellets, and reused. Within Europe similar schemes are being set up. In the UK over ten billion foam cups are used annually – about 40,000 tonnes of material. A Save-a-Cup scheme launched in London by cup producers quickly reached a recovery rate of one million cups a week, with a target of collecting 400 million cups by the end of 1994. The material is cleaned, pelletized and manufactured into trays, pots, coathangers, and office equipment.

Consumer pressure has forced manufacturers to drop their use of CFCs, but the alternatives are not without their hazards. Pentane is listed as a greenhouse gas and benzene, known to be carcinogenic, is used in making polystyrene. A different form of polystyrene is used in consumer durables and packaging items – from video and cassette boxes to clothes hangers. In Switzerland polystyrene is recycled into a filler for building materials.

Reuse/Recycle
Instead of using disposable cups, take a mug to work and don't buy disposable cups and plates for catering. Reuse polystyrene "chips" for packaging fragile gifts and write to manufacturers suggesting they use an alternative – shredded, low-grade paper is a good substitute. Polystyrene traps heat well, use **plastic** cups or trays for planting seeds. Support any collection projects in your neighbourhood.

POLYTHENE
Facts
The use of the polythylene resins, High Density Polythylene (HDPE) and Low Density Polythylene (LDPE) increases every year. Not only is more being used for manufacturing products, including **car** components and building materials, but **plastic** is a popular substitute for glass and metals. 62% of all plastic bottles in the US are made from HDPE.

The UK consumes over 1.5 million tonnes of polyolefins, the generic term for a wide range of common plastics, of which polythene is the most important. While factory scrap (preconsumer waste) is routinely recycled, the recycling of postconsumer waste is small. But the situation is changing rapidly as new products made from recycled HDPE appear on the market. When appearance is not vital the plastic is fully recycled into items such as drainpipes, flower pots, and traffic barrier cones. Other products, such as **bottles** for household detergents and industrial chemicals, are made with a percentage of recycled plastic mixed with virgin polymer. One UK company collects store retail waste for remanufacture into new products including carrier bags, rubbish sacks, and a unique range of Alphathene polythene raw materials – made from recycled post-use waste polythene. One use is self-sealing mailing bags and envelopes. Like most plastics petroleum oil is the basic raw material for polythene. Producing this type of plastic has less of an environmental impact than other types and ideally this is lessened even further through recovery programmes and recycling. However every time we use 1 tonne of recycled polythene in products, 1.8 tonnes of crude oil is saved.
Reuse
If there are no plastic collection schemes in your area, cut waste by looking for products in alternative **packaging**, or reuse as much as you can. Refill containers with the same product – bulk buy or take the container back to stores that operate a refill system. Don't reuse household cleaners or oil bottles for food or drink. Reuse polythene bags and other wrappings. Keep all plastic bags away from children; use dry-cleaning bags for storing clothes or as temporary covers for seed trays. Keep polythene sheets as protective covers for home decorating.

Recycle
Supermarkets may have collection banks for plastic bottles and
unwanted bags. Recycle if you cannot reuse. Support local plastics
recycling schemes. Check whether different types of plastics can be
mixed or have to be kept separate. It is not easy to identify plastics, but
try looking at the label or the container base, for a coding system.

PRECIOUS METALS RECOVERY
Facts
Industrial recovery schemes exist for a variety of precious metals.
Silver is a common element in photographic and printing operations
and large users may want to investigate its commercial recovery.
Computers and electrical circuitry are a source of **gold**, silver, and
palladium; although **salvage** from individual machines may not be
economic. Manufacturers often offer a recycling and disposal service.
In the UK one computer recovery programme currently retrieves 70%
by weight of the equipment processed, and along with individual
components such as motors and fans, metals recovered include gold,
silver, palladium, **copper**, **aluminium**, and stainless **steel**. Seek
professional advice from manufacturers on recovery programmes, or
look for specialist services in trade directories. **See also** Scrap
merchants

PULP see Wood pulp, Paper

PUSHCHAIRS/STROLLERS AND PRAMS
Facts
Baby conveyances today come in a wide variety of guises, from the
traditional pram, through a carrycot that can be fitted to a pushchair/
stroller and then replaced by a multi-positional reclining seat, to a basic
"umbrella fold" lightweight model. There is a certain amount of
planned obsolescence involved in pushchair/stroller design. For
example, the umbrella types are not suitable for babies under six
months of age, but many "reclining" designs, which are, are too
cumbersome to be folded into some cars and to take on public
transport. The idea that is conveyed by manufacturers is that parents

will need to purchase at least two pushchairs/strollers between baby-
and toddlerhood, and buy new models for any younger children. There
is no one model that suits all purposes at all ages.

Pushchairs/strollers are not always of the high quality needed to
withstand the hard use they get. But it is possible, with care and
maintenance, to make one stand up to most of the demands made of it
and then be saved for another baby.

Reuse/Recycle
Keep wheels oiled and check regularly to make sure they are not about
to fall off. Also check brakes regularly. Have large splits in **upholstery**
repaired professionally and patch small tears yourself (see p.135).
Many models have removable upholstery that can be washed. Beware
of adding to wear and tear by overloading pushchairs/strollers with
bags of heavy shopping, which can also topple the buggy and endanger
the child. Some stores offer a renovating service, but this usually only
applies to models in the current catalogue and is something of a
misnomer since they supply you with a new item rather than mend the
old one. It is relatively easy to buy good second-hand models in **charity
shops** and at car boot sales, and many local parent groups run a service
for swapping and selling all kinds of second-hand baby equipment.

PVC
Facts
The manufacture of polyvinyl chloride (PVC) differs from other
plastics; it is made from petroleum oil and salt, and releases toxic
vapours if burned. PVC is commonly used for **packaging** – including
plastic wrapping and **bottles**. Its adverse effects have led Sweden,
Austria, and the Netherlands to place restrictions on its use. In New
York the plastics industry lost a three-year battle against a ban on PVC
for disposable cups, dinnerware, and non-biodegradable plastic bags.
Polythene is a common substitute for **clingfilm/plastic wrap** and **PET**
or **polythene** for **bottles**. PVC itself is a substitute for **rubber** in
building materials and for footwear. The world's first recycling scheme
for Wellington boots has been established in the UK, where seven
million pairs are sold each year. Manufacturers plan to strip out the old
linings and remanufacture the PVC into new boots. Reclaimed PVC
from bottles is remanufactured into items such as sewer pipes.

Q

QUILTS
Facts
Patchwork and quilting date back many centuries and have always been popular forms of needlecraft and self expression. What began as a folk craft born of necessity, whereby warm bed coverings were made out of unwanted **rags**, is now a recognized art form.

Reuse/Recycle
You don't have to be a skilled designer to produce a quilt or cushion cover (see **Thrift project**) from leftover pieces of material, old **curtains**, old clothes, or scraps. Choose colours carefully and work out your design before you begin stitching.

Thrift project
How to make a hexagon patchwork quilt
- Cut out paper templates and pin to fabric.
- Cut around fabric, allowing extra for turnings.
- Tack fabric to templates or hold in place with masking tape.
- Stitch hexagons together using close overcast stitching.
- When the patchwork is complete, cut pieces of wadding/batting and backing fabric of the same size.
- Stitch the three layers together, either by tufting or by hand running stitches, which show on the right side.
- Bind the quilt edges together using bias-cut strips.

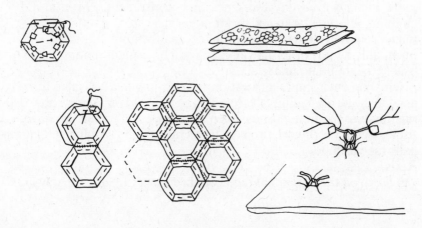

R

RADIOS
Facts
Valuable metals, including **copper**, are present in printed circuit boards, but unless equipment is past repair, reuse it rather than scrapping. If the radio works, but you do not want to keep it, give it to a second-hand outlet. The cheapness of new equipment cancels out any savings made by doing repairs, but mechanically minded people can reuse some components from dismantled equipment. Cut energy costs by using mains electricity rather than disposable **batteries**; or use rechargeables powered with solar power for portable radios.

RAGS
Facts
Approximately 4% of domestic rubbish consists of old **clothing**, **fabric** remnants, and unwanted furnishings. Much of this material should not end up in the **dustbin/garbage bin**. Worldwide there is a thriving textile reclamation trade, reusing or reprocessing all kinds of materials. The main sources of rags are the industrialized countries with high standards of living: Australia, Europe, Japan, and the US. Rags are fabrics past repair, and in these countries are usually regarded as "waste". But reprocessing a tonne of rags uses considerably less energy than manufacturing new fabrics; the end product is already found in many everyday items including **mattresses**, **carpets**, and clothing. A large market exists for industrial wiping cloths, usually made from recycled woven synthetics, and the lowest grades, unsuitable for any other purpose, can still be used in roofing felt, a waterproof building material.

Growing environmental awareness is leading to a revival in the ancient crafts of reusing fabric scraps and rags to make rag **rugs**, bags, rag dusters, and new clothes. Even the smallest fabric scraps have some use for patchwork projects (see **Quilts**), and making soft juggling balls (see p.159).
Reuse
Cut down on the amount of rags you throw away by buying only good-

quality, well-made clothes and soft furnishings. Give wearable garments to charities or thrift stores for resale, or to **jumble sales**. Avoid the need for disposable paper towels by reusing cotton rags for home cleaning and cleaning **bicycles** and **cars**. Old cotton shirts are ideal for this, but keep better-quality pieces for patchwork or repair jobs. Consider using brightly coloured scraps by making a colourful, hardwearing rag rug (see **Thrift project**).

Recycle

Recycle rather than throw away rags you cannot use. Children's **scrapstores** and playgroups can use clean fabric scraps for making puppets (see p.158), **toys,** and other craft projects. Rag merchants will collect large quantities left over after **jumble sales** and **charity stores** will usually accept smaller quantities for recycling. Rag banks are the final option: if there isn't a facility near by, press your local authority to provide one.

Thrift project

How to make a tufted rag rug
- Cut a piece of rag and fold it in half around the hook shaft. Insert the hook and pass it up underneath a thread of the backing fabric (coarse hessian is best).
- Take the two ends through the open latch and tuck them down under the hook.
- Pull the hook toward you so that the latch closes, until both ends are drawn through the loop to form a knot.
- Tug the two ends.

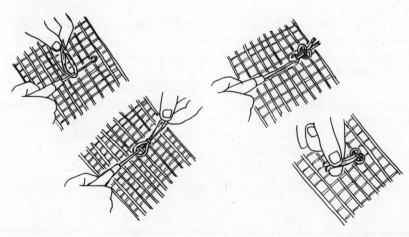

REED BED SYSTEMS
Facts
Every day **sewage** treatment works process large quantities of waste, including water, which has to be purified before it is released as effluent. Chemical treatment is costly and not always desirable. Consequently there is growing interest in using plants as pollution filters. Just one hectare of reeds will filter and purify the liquid effluent from 5000 people. The common reed, *Phragmites*, absorbs oxygen through its leaves and transmits this to its roots, where it enters the surrounding soil – a method known as the Root Zone Method. Toxic substances such as nitrates, phosphates, phenols, hydrocarbons, and mineral waste are extracted from the water by the reeds, which can also deal with harmful bacteria and **heavy metals**.

Reed bed systems resemble marshland and are environmentally very acceptable. Over 100 schemes exist in Germany and in the UK – several water companies are running experimental schemes at sewage treatment works.

Reuse/Recycle
Seek advice (see Resources) before attempting to reuse human waste as there is a potential serious health risk. If you cannot actually establish a reed bed system yourself, small-scale alternatives include **compost** and waterless toilets for rural locations, or places not connected to mains sewerage systems.

REFRIGERATORS
Facts
Most refrigerators and freezers are made of **steel**, a recyclable metal always in demand by **scrap merchants**. Yet every year many of these **white goods** end up being illegally dumped rather than recycled. Not only is this a waste of resources but every domestic refrigerator contains CFCs and HCFCs (their so-called safe replacement) are used in large-scale refrigeration systems. Refrigerators and other equipment are estimated to hold a vast bank of CFCs of at least 30,000 tonnes.

Most recovery programmes have only focused on draining the liquid coolant before scrapping, yet the newest refrigerators contain five times as much CFC in the foam insulation as in the coolant. This is only actually released when the machines are shredded.

The number of appliances sold every year is increasing; in the UK over two and a half million cooling units are sold every year, almost half of which are replacements for old appliances. Germany, Sweden, and the Netherlands have acted to ensure nationwide, mandatory CFC recovery, but in the UK only 3% of the total CFCs in fridges (22,000 tonnes) are actually being recovered by local authorities. New appliances containing reduced amounts of CFCs are available and models using 50% less electricity are on the market in Europe, Japan, and the US.

Reuse/Repair/Recycle

If you are thinking of buying a new refrigerator consider whether this is really necessary. Manufacturing them uses considerable amounts of energy and raw materials and ideally they should be changed only when they are no longer functioning properly. Extending their lifespan by reconditioning is the better option.

If you are buying a new appliance, find out whether the dealer will accept a trade-in, and whether the old equipment is recycled, plus CFC coolant. If they don't offer this service, buy elsewhere. When buying reconditioned equipment, it may be more economic to buy a new fridge with reduced CFC content and increased energy efficiency.

Regular cleaning increases efficiency. Studies show that after eighteen months, dust and fluff on an external condenser will increase the electricity use by 30%. Maintain your fridge by regular defrosting (if it is not self-defrosting), cleaning, and replace inefficient door seals.

Take unwanted equipment in working condition to **second-hand stores** or electrical refurbishment workshops. Repairs should only be done by a trained engineer. When operating normally, CFCs will not leak out of fridges. Recycling centres or scrap merchants will accept old equipment, but check first to make sure CFCs will be properly disposed of.

REFUSE-DERIVED FUEL (RDF)

Facts

About 30% of household waste in the UK is potentially combustible – suitable for burning to release energy. 2.6 tonnes of municipal waste is equivalent in calorific value to one tonne of coal if burned at equal efficiencies. The amount of energy, its calorific value, varies; **plastic** is the best, followed by **rags**, and **paper**. Metals and **glass** are not combustible and should always be separated for recycling.

Processing solid waste into fuel pellets is considered a form of recycling, but only if most economically viable recyclable materials are first eliminated. Waste too mixed or contaminated for separation can be used to fire industrial boilers, or to supply the fuel for energy-from-waste schemes. Burning waste prevents the formation of **landfill** gas, a mixture of methane and carbon dioxide. Both these gases are powerful greenhouse gases. If 40% of the UK's municipal waste (30 million tonnes) was burned as fuel, scientists estimate that the net environmental effect would be to prevent four million tonnes of landfill gas being produced every year. But burning waste can release **heavy metals** and other noxious substances, including **dioxins**. European legislation requires tight controls on new incinerators from 1995.

RESTORATION, OF OLD BUILDINGS
Facts
Restoration work often requires building materials that are no longer commonly available, or fittings that are expensive. Architectural **salvage** indexes are a source of quality material, particularly **wood** and old metal fixtures, which could be substituted instead.

Restoring a house entirely from recycled materials is possible, but requires creative imagination, persistence, and access to endless rubbish skips/dumpsters (see **Building materials**). For smaller-scale restoration try **jumble sales** and car boot sales, **second-hand stores**, unwanted wallpaper sample books from wallpaper and textile retailers, broken **tiles** from DIY stores and the local municipal tipping site.

Always try to use non-toxic products, or **adhesives** and preservative treatments that are the least environmentally damaging. Anything containing chemical solvents, including some glues and paints should be avoided. They are polluting to produce and can release vapours harmful to health.

REVERSE VENDING MACHINES

Cash for cans is the idea behind these machines. They pay the individual for returning drinks cans or **bottles** for recycling. It is a cost-effective method of recovering aluminium and is popular in Scandinavia, Austria, and Germany.

RUBBER
Facts

Use of natural latex rubber has declined as synthetic materials have captured a large percentage of industrial markets. Synthetic rubber demand was 10.73 million tonnes in 1990, with natural rubber consumption at 5.54 million tonnes. Malaysia produces about 78% of the world's supply of latex, exporting over 245,000 tonnes to 70 countries. The vehicle industry remains the largest user of natural rubber; but two-thirds of all rubber products are now made from the synthetic substitute. Natural rubber is making a comeback for radial **tyres**. Ways of reusing or recycling tyres have not kept pace with the growing volumes, which present a major disposal problem around the world.

RUBBISH see Solid waste

RUBBISH COMPACTORS (HOUSEHOLD)
Facts

Items such as **aluminium** drinks **cans** are bulky, so it makes sense to flatten them before recycling. By crushing cans you are able to store five times as many in the same place, saving trips to the recycling centre and cutting energy costs all round. Household can crushers, made of durable metal, are easily wall-mounted and are simple to operate. They do not require electricity.

RUGS
Facts
Rag rugs are a traditional floor covering, made from recycled worn **clothing** and textiles. These rugs were common before the existence of fitted **carpets** and are regaining their popularity as a creative reuse of materials. Rugs made of cotton, wool, sheepskin, and rush matting make durable floor coverings, prolonging the life of carpets if used in areas receiving heavy use. Synthetic fibres, including reclaimed materials, are often added to carpet mixtures to improve their resistance to wear.

Reuse/Repair/Recycle
Try making your own rag rug (see **Thrift project**). Keep **clothing** too worn for reuse or repair, try **jumble sales** for other fabrics, and use old bed linen and furnishing fabrics. A variety of colours and materials is the key to success.

Seek professional help for cleaning and repairing valuable antique or ethnic rugs; some of the **dyes** used may not be colourfast. Vegetable fibres such as sisal and rush are easily repaired; revive them by occasionally brushing with water and **detergent**. Give rugs in good condition to **second-hand stores**.

Thrift project
How to make a plaited rag rug
- Cut the fabric into strips 5-10 cm (2-4 in) wide. Fold and stitch the strips.
- Pin three strips together and begin plaiting.
- Coil the plait into a circle, oval, or rectangle and stitch together.

See **Rags** for how to make a tufted rag rug.

S

SALVAGE
Facts
Reclaiming materials from **demolition sites**, scrap heaps, rubbish tips, and the streets happens globally. Statistics do not exist for the amount of materials saved, but it substantially reduces the amount of reusable material ending up in **landfill** or **incineration**.

Throughout the world, salvaging goods is, for many people, an economic necessity, and for some, a means of survival. In most developing countries, salvage is practised to such an extent that nothing is wasted. Discarded **paper, plastics, glass**, metals, and **clothing** are valuable commodities, which if not directly reused, can be sold for reprocessing.

Reuse/Recycle
Salvage merchants, "totters", and "rag and bone" collectors accept just about anything that is likely to have a scrap value. **Ferrous metals** are always in demand; reusing scrap **steel** in steelmaking cuts the energy bill by 76%. And quality materials – salvaged **wood** and metalwork – have a growing market within the architecture and design professions. Although wood may weather with age, it retains a special quality. Salvage indexes list available items, or find them through auctions, sales, and antique markets. Other sources include old buildings, redundant churches, docks, building sites, and old farm sales. Office refurbishment schemes can yield skips/dumpsters full of discarded, serviceable furniture. Trade waste, particularly textiles, **plastic**, and paper offcuts are ideal for children's projects; industries with such materials to dispose of should donate them **scrapstores**, and resource centres. Alternatively give to **jumble sales, second-hand**, or thrift stores. Oxfam Wastesaver salvages textiles past repair for reprocessing into new fabrics or industrial wiping rags. And if you want to get hold of cheap furniture you can restore yourself think about buying from salvage yards.

Extend these ideas to your workplace. Find out what happens to the waste; could some be diverted to a local refurbishment scheme or salvage yard for reuse? **See also** Cars, Vehicle recycling

SAUCEPANS
Facts
Stainless **steel**, **aluminium**, cast **iron**, and **copper** are all worth
something as scrap when worn out. Stainless steel is easy to maintain,
but because it contains 10% chromium, it cannot be recycled with pure
steel. Cast-iron pots are very energy-efficient, but have a tendency to
rust as well as being very heavy. Copper looks attractive and conducts
heat well, but a poisonous green rust – verdigris – forms if pots are not
properly maintained. You should replace the tin (or **silver**) protective
lining every three years if you use the pans regularly.

Aluminium is always in demand by scrap metal merchants, but may
not be the safest metal to use when cooking certain acidic foods. These
have been found to react with the aluminium, causing small quantities
of the metal to leach into food or water. The actual health hazard has
yet to be assessed, but a strong link is suspected between aluminium
and Alzheimer's disease (premature senility).

Reuse/Repair/Recycle
Buy a basic set of high-quality, long-lasting pans rather than cheaper
versions that wear out faster. Prolong the life of your equipment by
proper cleaning; re-tinning services are offered at many specialist
cookware stores. Check and tighten the screws on handles and lids
regularly. Don't use faulty equipment; if handles are past repair, find
another use for pans – they make ideal **dye** baths or plant pot holders.
Or give them to **scrap merchants** or recycling centres.

SCRAP MERCHANTS
Facts
Scrap yards are well-established businesses within the reclamation
trade, supplying separated secondary materials, mostly metals, for
reuse or recycling. Scrap is an important resource, cutting demand for
more raw materials, and reducing energy use in processes such as steel
manufacture. In the UK, recycling ferrous scrap saves ten million
tonnes of finite raw materials, ten million tonnes worth of **landfill**, and
1.4 billion gallons of petrol (energy equivalent) every year. Over two
million vehicles and 5.2 million **white goods** are reprocessed annually.

Old vehicles, building materials, and white goods (**cookers/stoves**,
washing machines, **refrigerators**) provide a constant supply of scrap

iron and steel. Aluminium fetches a higher price and is always in demand, as is copper and brass. Mixtures of metals fetch lower prices. Some scrap merchants accept non-metals including rags and woollens (see Wool and woollen goods) for selling on to the textile reclamation trade. The smaller merchants buy directly from individuals and "totters", and sell the compacted, shredded, and dismantled scrap on to larger concerns who have regular contracts with steelworks.

Generally, the price of materials does not reflect their social costs. For example, the environmental impact of mining and smelting metal ores, and the energy-intensive manufacturing processes. Reuse and recycling always helps cut this impact. Not all scrap is post-consumer or "obsolete" scrap (this is the most difficult type to recycle because of contamination by other materials), production, or factory waste, "home scrap", is of a guaranteed quality and can be fed directly back in to production processes.

Reuse/Repair/Recycle

If you are mechanically minded, dismantle old motors, engines, and vehicles. Save useful parts and separate the rest for scrap. Some merchants will collect. Visit local scrap merchants if you want replacement parts for cars or machinery. Ask at the gate or guarantee your entrance by taking some scrap along to sell. Alternatively buy directly from "totters" on the street.

If you are doing house repairs or building work, it is worth checking salvage yards or auctions for quality wood, construction materials, and fixtures and fittings. Prices will be much lower than buying new and the quality may be better.

SCRAPSTORES
Facts

Children's scrapstores were set up to creatively reuse all sorts of safe waste – rolls of paper, card, fabric offcuts, plastic components, tubes, and cardboard packaging. The more imaginative the better. Every day, large quantities of these materials are thrown away in factories and offices. Without reuse, much ends up as landfill or is incinerated. But a scrapstore or children's play centre will convert the waste into a treasure trove of new opportunities. The universal scrapstore slogan is "Don't throw it away, give it to play!"

Reuse/Recycle

Look around your home or workplace. Are there large quantities of non-toxic materials you regularly throw out? If you are not reusing, refilling, returning, or recycling them, find out where your nearest scrapstore is, or check whether a local school could use them. Scrapstores accept all quantities – from a crate to a vanload.

SECOND-HAND STORES

Facts

In an age of "conspicuous consumption", advertising pressures persuade us to replace many items way before they are worn out. Consequently there is a thriving second-hand market, especially for household appliances and furniture. Second-hand, or thrift, stores divert reusable materials away from waste disposal or illegal dumping (**flytipping**) and many undertake all sorts of repairs, reconditioning, and restoration. Buying second-hand does not necessarily mean you are buying a product of inferior quality – choose carefully and be aware that many consumers' rights extend to second-hand items, too.

Reuse/Recycle

Before replacing or upgrading electrical or household appliances, consider whether you really need to change them. Could you extend the life of equipment by having it repaired? Get professional advice if you aren't sure, but beware of dealers just trying to sell you a new piece of equipment. If you want to replace items, ask to trade-in the old model as part payment for the new. This saves you from having to dispose of old appliances. They are then sold on to dealers for reconditioning, or sent to be dismantled for scrap.

If a second-hand purchase breaks down shortly after you've bought it, take it back to the shop – second-hand goods are usually covered by legislation, so you should be entitled to a refund, replacement, or the cost of repairs. If you are buying a second-hand **car**, have it inspected by an expert before agreeing to the sale. Scrap yards are a source of salvaged spare parts. **See** Charity stores

SEEDS
Facts
As multinationals develop new strains of seed with long-life and pest-resistant properties, traditional varieties of plants are becoming displaced. And with time, it is feared that such practices could weaken the gene pool. Seed saving is an established practice and a guaranteed way of getting organic seed, as well as saving money.
Reuse/Recycle
Collect seed from flowering plants for reuse next planting season. To be successful you must store it in dry conditions; organic growing organizations (see Resources), or Seed Savers Exchange (US) provide advice on such matters and operate a seed bank and exchange scheme. Save and share seed with neighbours or through community garden or allotment schemes. Keep glass **jars** for this purpose.

SEWAGE
Facts
Recycling human wastes may not be an appealing idea, but as the volume of sewage increases every year, we need to develop ways of maximizing its use. Sewage is not just solid material. Up to 99% is water; including industrial effluent, water from baths and **washing machines**, and rain water. It is extremely rich in nutrients; in the wrong place, for example rivers, the high content of nitrogen makes it very polluting. But if used with care, it makes an excellent fertilizer. Reusing **nightsoil** in this way is an ancient practice in Asia.

At sewage treatment works, **paper** and **plastic** is screened out and biological systems, based on bacteria, are left to break down solids. Some treatment techniques use plants, such as *Phragmites*, in special reed beds for the purification process. In India, the water hyacinth serves a similar process. Treated effluent, or "clean water", is released into rivers and streams and the sludge is available as a land fertilizer. However the presence of **heavy metals** in industrial effluents is not removed by sewage treatment, limiting the reuse of sludge on agricultural land. The UK is the only European country still dumping sewage sludge at sea; this practice has been banned by the European Community from 1998. Half of the UK's sewage sludge is currently spread on farmland, the rest is either dumped untreated into the sea or

landfilled. Alternative disposal methods used by other countries include incineration and composting with other materials such as municipal waste or straw to form a soil conditioner or **compost**.
Reuse/Recycle
Compost toilets make small-scale sewage recycling possible; human wastes are mixed with sawdust or woodchips and left to compost. Waterless toilets are another innovative technology, reducing pressure on our overloaded sewerage systems. These do not need to be connected to drains or cesspits and are ideal for rural locations, or where suitable sanitation facilities do not exist. They work by dehydrating solids down to 10% of their original volume, and by evaporating liquids into a gaseous mixture, which is expelled through a vent pipe. The solid matter is then left to compost. Information on compost or waterless toilets can be obtained from a variety of organizations and manufacturers (see Resources). **See** Compost toilets, Manure, Reed bed systems, Vermiculture

---

SHOES AND BOOTS
Facts
Footwear is generally hard to recycle because of the variety of materials and **adhesives** used in the manufacturing process. The traditional materials of **leather** and **rubber** are losing out to cheaper **plastic** and **PVC** substitutes. In order to limit this impact, one major Wellington boot manufacturer runs a recycling service in the UK for PVC boots. They are collected through special collection banks and returned for shredding and remoulding into new boots. This echoes a traditional practice found in many developing countries, where rubber car **tyres** are cut up to make the soles and straps of shoes. The distinctive Moroccan slipper frequently displays internationally famous tyre brand names on its underside.
Reuse/Recycle
Extending the life of shoes by appropriate care and reuse is the best option. Leather cracks if it isn't polished; look for polishes in tins rather than in aerosols, and give leather shoes a chance to "breathe" after use. Shoes last longer and keep their shape if you have repairs done as soon as possible and refrain from wearing the same pair day after day.

Give unwanted footwear to **charity stores**, or **jumble sales**. But bear in mind that children should really have new shoes bought specially for them after precise measuring and fitting by a trained professional.

SHORTLIFE GOODS
Facts
We use many items that have a very limited lifespan, yet are manufactured from high-quality raw materials. Some use is totally inappropriate. For example, using virgin **wood pulp** for **toilet paper** when a perfectly acceptable substitute can be made from low-grade waste **paper**.

Many disposable products are not necessary; not only do they need disposal but their manufacture uses resources and energy that could be put to better use elsewhere. Or even better, not used at all. And while some items are recognizably shortlife, other products that are meant to last do not because of poor-quality materials and shoddy design. Such built-in obsolescence is becoming a feature of life in industrialized countries. Manufacturers no longer stock replacement units or the spare parts essential for repairs – so unless an identical piece is found at a **salvage** yard or cannibalized from another machine, the broken equipment or machine is usually redundant, and sometimes only useful as scrap.

Reduce/Reuse/Repair/Recycle
Limit or stop using unnecessary disposable items. Buy good-quality items that last, rather than gimmicks. Initially, they may cost more, but in the long run, they will save you money on replacements. Find out if manufacturers offer product guarantees and repair services. Extend the life of goods; clean appliances regularly following the manufacturer's instructions and if you can, tackle small repairs yourself. Look for repair manuals in your local library. For bigger jobs, and anything involving electrics, seek professional help. Take appliances and furniture beyond repair to waste disposal sites or scrapyards.

SHREDDERS
Facts
A shredder enables you to transform **garden/backyard waste** into material suitable for composting or **mulch**. Shredding splits the wood fibres, assisting a quicker breakdown of materials on your **compost** heap. Diverting organic materials away from **landfill** is an important waste-reduction strategy; composting dramatically cuts the volume of waste needing disposal and recycles nutrients back into the soil. It also helps prevent **landfill gas**, a major contributor to global warming.

Shredding and chipping is a well-established practice in the US and Germany. Many US states ban the dumping of yard waste (garden rubbish) and leaves in landfill sites. Instead they are collected separately for composting at municipal sites.
Reuse/Recycle
Buy or hire small shredders from garden centres or hardware stores. They will easily shred soft prunings from trees and shrubs, woody stem plants, grass clippings, and leaves; for larger pieces of wood hire a chipper. Commercial-sized shredders are suitable for wooden pallets and crates, and the type of wood found at **demolition sites**. Remember that the end product is only as good as the original material; if this contains contaminants, for example nails, screws, or paint, it won't be suitable for composting. **See also** Building materials

---

SILVER
Facts
Most of the world's silver-bearing deposits are found in South America, with identified reserves totalling about 770,000 tonnes. Silver is a precious metal with a high scrap value. Its familiar uses include **jewellery**, decorative ornaments, and silverplate **cutlery** and tableware. As one of the best conductors of electricity, silver is extensively used in all forms of electronics, including printed circuit boards, as well as in photographic films.
Reuse
If your workplace uses large amounts of film, cut costs by switching to black and white silverless film, or implement a programme to reclaim the silver. Contact a precious metals recovery firm for details.

There is a thriving second-hand market for silver items – if you are buying, always look for the hallmark to determine whether it is pure silver or plate. Repairs and replating are professional jobs, so take items to a silversmith. Silver tarnishes easily, restore the shine with a soft cloth and proprietary silver cleaner – or polish jewellery with a little toothpaste, pure alcohol, or surgical spirit.

SOAP SCRAPS
Reuse/Recycle
Although these may seem too small to mention, why discard something that is easy to reuse? Either press the slivers into a new bar of soap or collect them in a jam jar until you have enough to make a soap solution for handwashing delicate clothes or general household cleaning. Just add a little warm water to the soap and shake the jar.

SOIL ADDITIVES
Facts
Leaves, garden/backyard waste and certain food scraps are recyclable. By using a **compost** heap, making leafmould (see **Humus**), or using worms (see **Vermiculture**) to break down the organic matter into a soil conditioner or compost, you are using natural methods to return nutrients to the soil, as well as improving its structure. Other organic matter has the same effect. **Sewage**, on its own or composted with solid waste or straw, produces a rich soil conditioner – the only drawback is the **heavy metal** content of some industrial effluents ending up in sewage. Applying animal manure is a traditional means of increasing a soil's fertility. **See also** Compost, Organic waste.

SOLAR POWER
Facts
In many countries solar water heating is a well-established technology; these systems actively tap the sun's heat through the use of roof or wall solar panels. Flat plate collectors will pay for themselves within five to fifteen years, depending on your hot water consumption. More

sophisticated systems, which may be computer-controlled, are evacuation tubes. For the mechanically minded, DIY systems can be built much more cheaply. Plans are available from alternative technology organizations (see Resources).

But equally important are passive solar technologies; a south-facing room heats up much faster than a north-facing one (or vice versa in the southern hemisphere). And once you've got the heat, keep it in, at the very least by **draughtproofing** or putting up heavy **curtains**. More than half our winter heating bills could be met by just using passive solar and energy conservation techniques. Double-glazing, painting concrete walls dark colours to absorb the sun's heat, and using solar battery chargers for rechargeable **batteries** are all low-cost options. Many appliances such as torches, lighting, and even televisions can be solar-powered.

Photovoltaics – whereby a number of solar cells are connected together to produce electricity for charging batteries, or to power electrical DC equipment – are considered an appropriate technology.

SOLID WASTE
Facts
The European Community generates over 2000 million tonnes of waste a year, 80% of this is potentially reusable or recyclable as raw materials or energy. The UK generates 30 million tonnes of domestic and commercial waste every year, compared to 40 million tonnes in Japan and the 195.7 million tonnes in the US. **Landfill** and **incineration** are the usual disposal routes, but rising costs and tighter legislation makes greater reuse and recycling an economic necessity. This is reflected in the US, where the overall recycling rate (including composting) reached 47% in 1990, the latest official figures available.

Different countries have varying percentages of wastes. Legislation keeps materials such as **bottles**, **cans**, and **garden/backyard waste** out of landfill in some countries. And easy access to recycling facilities is another factor. But culture and poverty also play an important role in the reuse of materials. In many parts of the world, one person's waste is another's resource – in Cairo the Zabbaleen make a living from scavenging **paper**, **plastic**, and metal from the city's rubbish tips.

Waste reduction is the only effective solution. Selective buying, precycling, design for recycling, reuse, and remanufacturing are essential strategies. Composting even a fraction of organic waste reduces volume and creates a valuable soil conditioner. Energy from waste schemes save fossil fuel reserves; 2.6 tonnes of municipal solid waste replaces 1 tonne of coal if burned at equal efficiencies. And if solid waste is too mixed or contaminated for reuse, energy from waste is a viable option.

Reuse/Repair/Recycle

Take a look at the typical contents of your **dustbin/garbage bin**. Are you throwing away reusable items? Could you cut down on the amount of **packaging** you buy and discard? In the US, packaging accounts for 13% of food costs and 50% of rubbish costs. Keep unwanted **clothing** or textiles for the next **jumble sale** or donate to charity. Use the back of torn **envelopes** as scrap paper for shopping lists and reuse others with envelope reuse stickers. Take containers, such as **egg cartons**, and **bottles** back for reuse.

Separate waste at source – in the home or workplace. If you haven't got a **compost** heap, start one. **See** Organic waste, Vermiculture

---

SPECTACLES

Facts

Several major aid agencies and charities collect spectacles (glasses) for distribution in developing countries. Some opticians are part of the collection network. Or contact organizations such as Oxfam and Community Aid Abroad.

Repairs to spectacles need to be done by an expert, but in an emergency use clear adhesive tape to hold broken frames together. Prevent having to make more serious repairs by occasionally tightening the screws of spectacles.

SPORTS EQUIPMENT

Facts

Expensive equipment bought in the first flush of enthusiasm for a sport is often inappropriate, or unnecessary. Avoid costly mistakes by buying only recommended equipment when you know you are really going to

use it a lot. Until then, borrow or hire, and look for quality second-hand items – check noticeboards at sports centres for unwanted equipment.
Reuse
Extend the life of equipment by regular cleaning and have repairs done as soon as necessary. Sports equipment stores sell repair materials for replacing frayed handle grips, but more complicated jobs, such as restringing, will need to be done professionally.

Schools and community youth groups will be able to reuse any unwanted equipment.

STAMPS
Facts
Used postage stamps are worth money to charities, so don't throw them away. There is a big market for all sorts of stamps, especially less-common foreign ones. Find out what sort charities need and start collecting. Cut them off **envelopes** (save for reuse or as scrap paper) and keep them until you have a reasonable quantity to donate. Encourage other people to collect, too.

STEEL
Facts
Steel is the most commonly used metal in the world and scrap-metal recycling is one of the oldest recycling industries. In 1989-90, the world produced over 783 million tonnes of raw steel. Over 320 million tonnes of **iron** and steel is recycled every year. Steel is Europe's most recycled packaging material; average recycling rates are 25% with 50% in Germany and 30% in Belgium.

As much as 25% of all the material routinely used in steel-making is scrap metal; some furnaces can use nearly 100% scrap. The principal raw materials are iron ore, limestone, and coal – all finite resources. But by replacing iron ore with scrap metal, energy savings of up to 76% are achievable. Newer methods, such as continuous casting, give even greater energy savings – up to 80%. Steel cans require less energy to produce than **aluminium**, use less raw materials.

Other savings are also significant. Using ferrous scrap saves the UK ten million tonnes of raw materials every year, and diverts ten million tonnes of potential ferrous waste away from **landfill**. The byproducts are reused at every stage of steel-making. The highest value scrap is pre-consumer waste; metal shavings are uncontaminated with other metals and thus highly recyclable.

Steel-making is polluting, but low sulphur coal and the use of gas recycling techniques can reduce this impact. Contaminants are a barrier to increased recycling – for example, scrap salvaged from **demolition sites** and vehicle manufacture will contain other metals or **plastics** and the **tin** used as a rust-proof coating on steel food and drinks **cans** has to be removed before reprocessing steel. New technologies are constantly being developed to combat such problems.

Other steel-containing products need special treatment before recycling. The US Environmental Protection Agency has raised concern over **white goods** such as **freezers** and **refrigerators**. Reputable scrap merchants remove ozone-depleting CFCs before crushing steel.

Steel forms the backbone of modern industry. Besides its uses in the construction and automobile industry, steel is a basic component of many household appliances and packaging. 25% of every steel drinks can is recycled metal.

Reuse/Recycle

Support steel recycling schemes. Test food or drinks cans with a magnet. Some cans are a mixture of aluminium and tinplate steel so always test the body, not the top of the can. Old **cars, cookers/stoves**, and **washing machines** are worth something to a **scrap merchant**.

Before replacing cookers/stoves, refrigerators, and other white goods, find out if they could be reconditioned to give another couple of years' use. If not, trade in for new or second-hand items. Many local authorities accept unwanted fridges and cookers/stoves for disposal at civic amenity sites. **See also** Cans

---

STONE
Facts

The building trade uses and wastes large quantities of stone in construction work and at **demolition sites**. Practices at building sites are generally not selective; reusable stone gets mixed in with low-grade rubble and soil. But salvaging higher-value materials is increasingly more attractive due to rising waste disposal costs. Obtaining quarried marble, limestone, sandstone, and granite has a substantial impact on surrounding countryside and transporting it to processing plants is energy-intensive.

Reuse
If you are building garden walls, rockeries, or terraces, look for second-hand stone or broken paving slabs at stone merchants or **salvage** yards. Even small pieces can be used for crazy paving paths, plant borders, or for edging lawns. Patterned limestones are ideal for **mosaic** decorations. Recycled stone is generally very durable and much cheaper than new.

Repair
Marble has a tendency to stain and limestones are affected by weak acids and alkalis. Remove stains on stone flooring quickly, wash or scour with a mild abrasive, lemon juice, or vinegar. Badly stained marble will need professional treatment; machine-grinding removes damaged surfaces, restoring original colour and texture.

STRAW
Facts
In the UK, over six million tonnes of surplus straw is disposed of every year, often by burning. From 1992, this agricultural practice was banned. Straw can be reused in a variety of ways – as a **mulch**, for animal fodder, or bedding, as well as for crop protection. Straw is also used in papermaking.

Alternatives to burning include composting with sewage sludge or manure, and using it for the industrial production of cellulose. Straw is a major component of an "environment-friendly" rigid particle board. Free of formaldehyde, the manufacturers claim that it is suitable for packaging, building materials, and furniture. In Germany, a company is producing straw-based protective packaging – the manilla bags are filled with straw, which is compostible after use.

Reuse/Recycle
Use straw for animal bedding or as a frost protector in the garden. Don't dig it into soil, it can deplete the nitrogen content. Straw bought from farms is likely to contain herbicide residues, so leave it to weather for at least six months before use.

T

TABLES
Facts
You can make all sorts of junk into table tops, desks, or workbenches. With two simple trestles you can convert any flat surface, for example a door, into a table. And with a little imagination, the right tools, and access to **salvage** yards, **demolition sites**, or rubbish skips/dumpsters, you can make new furniture out of waste materials. Offices going through refurbishment regularly discard quality furniture and wood suitable for desk tops. Keep an eye open for skips/dumpsters or go into offices and ask if anything is being thrown out. Some businesses are more than willing to let furniture go to a good home, rather than on to the scrap heap, and others regularly donate unwanted furniture to charities.

Reuse old doors or **wood** from salvage yards for workbenches; use two-drawer filing cabinets, sturdy tea chests, or shelving as the supports. Search antique markets and auctions for tables, cut the legs down for coffee tables, or refurbish by stripping down to the natural wood and repolishing or staining.

Reuse
Restore badly marked wood by sanding it down and revarnishing or repainting it. Be careful when stripping old paintwork, it may contain lead. Use non-toxic **paints** and techniques such as rag-rolling to give an interesting marbled finish. If the table is too badly damaged, cover it with fabric; search sales for remnants of bold, colourful prints, or drape with an old velvet curtain. You can make a heatproof surface with small **tiles**, or design a **mosaic**.

Repair
With care, good-quality wood can last for years. Use a wood filler for small cracks, and replace badly split planks with second-hand **timber**. Never buy new tropical timbers.

Recycle
Give tables to **second-hand stores**, charities, or **jumble sales**. Wood recycling facilities are now found at many civic amenity sites.

TELEPHONES
Facts
Telecommunication companies run recovery and recycling schemes for reusing the variety of materials found in telephones. In the UK, where over 3.5 million telephones are dismantled every year, about 85% of the material content (by weight) is recovered. One of the most unlikely end uses is the **glass** from old payphone housings, which is recycled into dental fillings. The outer body, made of a high-quality **plastic** (ABS), is granulated and reformulated into complex mouldings such as printer ribbon cassettes. The metallic content is not wasted – **copper** coils and brass components are removed and magnetic extraction deals with the steel. The printed circuit boards, usually coated in **gold**, contain other precious metals, including palladium and **silver**. Design for easier recycling is being investigated.
Reuse
Always return broken telephones to the supplier for recycling. Older bakelite models are found in antique market stalls and are sought after for their decorative value.

TELEPHONE DIRECTORIES
Facts
Every year huge amounts of **paper** are used to make telephone directories. Until recently few were printed on recycled paper, and recycling was difficult because of the **adhesives** (see also **Contraries and stickies**) used in the bindings. If the US recycled just one year's supply of phone books, an estimated 650,000 tonnes of paper would be saved.

Making these bulky items recyclable is a priority for the telecommunications industry. Experiments with different layouts and smaller typefaces have meant that less paper is used, but although a step in the right direction, this is no substitute for recycling. Illinois in the US has been using recycled paper since 1990 – over 14 million pages for the 1990 edition – and in San Francisco the city is working with Pacific Bell to promote the recycling of old phone books, which are made with water-based glues and no other contaminants in the covers. In Australia, the 20 million directories use 60,000 tonnes of paper annually, but only one-third end up at recycling centres.

In an effort to find new uses for the reclaimed paper, a pilot project is producing building insulation material from shredded directories. The end product, treated to make it fire-resistant, is 25% cheaper than traditional insulation materials and is already selling well.

Reuse/Recycle
Unless local waste paper collections will accept phone books, there may be no alternative but to put them in the **dustbin/garbage bin**. When you pay your phone bill, ask what your local company is doing to make recycling easier. If you have an open fire, use the paper for firelighters.

TELEVISION (TV)
Facts
Advertising pressure is a great persuader, convincing people to upgrade their existing equipment to more sophisticated models with public information services such as Ceefax. Hence many TVs are discarded well before they are worn out. In 1989, a study revealed that one-quarter of all TV sets (plus **refrigerators** and **washing machines**) found on UK scrapheaps had no obvious fault. A further quarter could have been repaired for a nominal amount and an hour's work. And one in ten of all the discarded machines were models still for sale in stores.

Generally the average colour TV is not as energy-efficient as it could be. Most use 150kWh of electricity per year (assuming they are switched on for three hours a day) yet in Japan manufacturers are producing models that only consume 40kWh. Leaving a TV on standby, rather than switching it off properly, continues to consume up one-quarter of the energy used when fully switched on. Friends of the Earth (UK) estimate that this wasted energy costs millions every a year and generates almost 200,000 additional tonnes of carbon dioxide, a major contributor to the greenhouse effect.

Reuse/Repair/Recycle
TV sets emit electromagnetic radiation. Some experts suggest that this might be harmful, so don't use faulty equipment or sit too close to the screen. Never attempt repairs yourself, even when the set is unplugged; it can be dangerous. Take the set to an repair store. If you hire the TV, it is likely that your contract covers free repair or exchange. Reputable dealers will recondition and sell second-hand equipment – if you buy such a TV, get a receipt in case it breaks down

shortly after purchase. Consumers have rights if they are sold faulty second-hand equipment. Dispose of working TVs at **second-hand** or **charity stores**, sell at a car boot sale or give to a **jumble sale**.

TEXTILES see Fabrics and textiles

TIGHTS/PANTYHOSE AND STOCKINGS
Facts
Although a small item, large numbers are sold around the world. In the UK alone, 500 million pairs are sold each year – about 23 pairs for each woman. Nylon is a synthetic substance that is not biodegradable. Its production is thought to be responsible for up to 10% of the increase in atmospheric nitrous oxide gas – an important greenhouse gas.
Reuse/Recycle
Tights/pantyhose and stockings are shortlife items that are difficult to repair. Two pairs can be combined by cutting off one laddered leg from two identical pairs and wearing them together. Or cut them up and reuse as a stuffing for children's **toys**, for cushions, or make a kneeling pad for gardening out of an old hot water bottle stuffed with tights/pantyhose. Alternatively use them for staking garden plants and for weaving rag rugs (nylon can be dyed). Some people tie up their bundles of **newspapers** with nylons, but check with your paper collector first – nylon is not biodegradable, so it can contaminate the recycling process.

TILES
Facts
Tiles serve both a decorative and practical purpose. In kitchens and bathrooms they help protect walls from water splashes or cooking stains, and quarry tiles provide a long-lasting floor covering, resistant to heat and chipping. Tiles are easy to replace, making them ideal for restoring or revamping surfaces. Small, broken pieces make a decorative wall or floor **mosaic** (see **Thrift project**).

Hardware or specialist stores sell a wide variety of tiles – ceramics, **cork**, slate, **linoleum**, **plastic**, **PVC**, **carpet** tiles, **mirrors**, and even **wood** tiles for flooring. Look for old-fashioned, hand-painted tiles in antique shops and flea markets. PVC flooring emits vapours that can irritate the respiratory system; they should be avoided by asthma-sufferers, or use a special non-toxic sealing polish.

Manufacturing coloured **cullet** into hard-wearing tiles is a popular reuse of materials in developing countries. In Mexico waste glass is mixed with cement to form a high-quality tile, although fly ash, broken china, and porcelain from crushed sinks and toilet bowls, and even dried **sewage** sludge, can be used as the filler.

Reuse/Repair/Recycle
Give rooms a new look by replacing a few tiles with decorative hand-painted designs, or completely re-tile an existing tiled surface. Check first to make sure the original tiles are not loose or chipped, remove any broken ones by chipping them out. If you keep left-over cork or **linoleum** tiles, you can patch damaged areas in your flooring, or use cork shavings from **bottle tops**. If you cannot find any matching material, cut a piece from an area hidden from view by furniture. Always try to use non-toxic **adhesives**.

Thrift project
How to make a mosaic-tiled surface
- Use a notched trowel to spead the tile adhesive.
- Working across the area embed the tile pieces in the adhesive to your chosen design, keeping the surface as even as possible.
- When the adhesive has set, use a sponge to work the grout in.

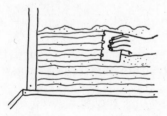 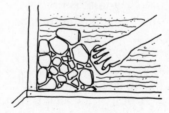

TIMBER
Facts
Wood is a durable material that can be reused and recycled many times. Although it is a renewable resource, many forestry practices are unsustainable, creating long-term environmental damage. The practice of monoculture – growing plantations of a single tree species for wood pulp or timber – is now very common. Nowhere is safe from commercial pressures. Some of the richest habitats in the world – for example, old-growth forest in British Columbia is being devastated solely to feed the **paper** industry. And despite world attention on the plight of diminishing tropical rainforests, short-term economic priorities continue to receive precedence over the long-term sustainability.

Countries such as Japan and the UK are large consumers of tropical hardwoods. Every year the timber trade is directly responsible for the loss of vast tracts of rainforest. Refrain from buying tropical hardwoods; teak, iroko, ramin, and mahogany are commonly used in the furniture and building industry. Thankfully consumer awareness has encouraged more enlightened timber merchants to stock a range of alternatives, including temperate hardwoods (ash, beech, and walnut are durable woods) and softwoods (pine, larch, and fir). Some major furniture retailers and do-it-yourself stores have already banned, or are in the process of phasing out, tropical hardwoods from their stores; others have implemented voluntary labelling schemes, providing information on the origin of the timber, and for softwoods the forestry management regime. But determining whether any type of timber comes from a sustainable source is always going to be extremely difficult.

Timber substitutes from waste-based materials are coming on to the market. For example, imitation wood made from mixed plastic waste is rot-proof, long-lasting, and suitable for fencing, poles, and garden furniture; its only drawback is that it cannot take the heavy weights that wood can hold. Other waste-based products include a rigid particle board manufactured from straw and agricultural waste, and a board made entirely from recycled paper fibre. These are suitable for a wide range of building uses and are preferable to hardboard as they do not release toxic formaldehyde vapours.

Reuse/Repair/Recycle
If you want timber for repairs, furniture-making, or DIY work, try a local **salvage** company or second-hand timber yard. Many have stocks of well-seasoned wood, ready for use and at low prices. Community refurbishment schemes accept donations of wooden furniture and chairs for repair or re-upholstery. Refurbished goods are usually sold to local charities. Alternatively give wood that is free from nails or splinters to local community groups, environmental improvement projects, or children's **scrapstores**.

Take unwanted timber to a civic amenity site or recycling centre. The waste disposal authority usually sells the wood to **salvage** merchants or sends it to **landfill** or **incineration**. Burning potentially reusable timber is not recycling; avoid doing it unless the wood is diseased. Great care should be taken with any wood burning as toxic substances, such as **dioxins**, may be present in the smoke. Do not put old painted timber on **bonfires** – leaded paint will flake off in the heat.

TIN
Facts
Tin is used in metal **alloys** of bronze and pewter, and more commonly in tinplate steel. The tin layer prevents rust. It is a highly polished metal that needs careful cleaning or restoration by retinning. **See** Saucepans

---

TIN CANS
Facts
Tin **cans** are actually made of tinplate, a special grade of **steel** coated with a thin layer of tin to stop rusting. Recycling these cans saves 74% of the energy used to originally produce them from raw materials and today 25% of every new can is recycled steel. Detinning before recycling recovers up to 70% of the available tin. **See also** Cans, Steel

---

TOILET PAPER
Facts
Direct reuse or recycling is not an option, but far too much of this disposable **paper** is made from virgin wood pulp, processed at great

cost to the environment. Our future use of paper must be based on the idea of the "right use for the right grade" of paper. The alternative to virgin pulp is to use 100% unbleached, low-grade wastepaper to manufacture toilet paper. This not only cuts pollution and energy use but ensures that high-grade waste paper is not being flushed down the toilet. Buying toilet paper manufactured from low-grade waste encourages the market for such products.

Some manufacturers have always used a certain percentage of recycled fibre in toilet paper (and other disposable paper products), but have never publicized the fact for fear of consumer resistance. Others continue to justify their use of virgin pulp by emphasizing the need for product purity. This is not a valid argument, but too many people still support such manufacturers. **See also** Paper

---

TOOLS
Facts
Extending the use of materials demands all sorts of tools, but unless you earn your living from restoration work it is not really necessary to buy many. Cut consumption and the time spent on maintenance by getting hold of a basic set of the highest-quality tools you can afford, and borrow or hire specialist tools as needed.

Just having access to the right tools is difficult in some developing countries. The few that are available in larger towns may cost two or three times their usual price in Europe. Tools for Self Reliance (UK) uses volunteer labour to collect and refurbish tools; over 40,000 individual items are dealt with each year. Tool sets are made up and sent to parts of the world where they are most needed.
Reuse/Recycle
All sorts of tools are always in demand so try not to hoard unwanted equipment; donate it to charity or refurbishment workshops, or take it to **second-hand stores**. Arrange a tool collection in your area, or help at an existing charity scheme. Keep equipment in good working order with regular cleaning, oiling, and sharpening. Sharpen hand tools with a carborundum stone, but regrinding and overhauling power tools is best done professionally to avoid accidents. Replace rotten wooden handles and don't discard items when broken – get them repaired. Or dismantle those past repair for useful spare parts.

TOYS/PLAY EQUIPMENT
Facts

All sorts of unwanted household materials – cereal packets, **cardboard** boxes, toilet roll tubes, coloured **magazines**, card, string, **newspaper**, cotton reels, gift wrapping, old **clothing**, and even dried foods such as pulses, are the basic materials for many easy-to-make toys. Make cuddly toys from fabric remnants, unravel old **wool** jumpers and reknit, or even use odd socks to make soft toys (see **Thrift project**). Use old tights/pantyhose or cotton scraps as the soft filling. More sophisticated items can be made from scrap **wood** or metal, or unwanted matchboxes decorated with non-toxic paints. Children can use papier mâché to make fun things that will last longer if given a coat of varnish after painting (see **Thrift project**). Many traditional toys in India and Africa are made from waste paper or metal wire, and papier mâché is common throughout Asia.

If you run a play scheme or youth project, joining a children's **scrapstore** or resource centre will give you unlimited access to all sorts of safe, non-toxic waste donated by retail outlets and factories for imaginative play and art projects. Toy libraries, whereby toys are lent out like books, so that children can have access to toys for free, exist in many places.

Reuse/Repair/Recycle

Swapping toys with friends or borrowing them from a toy library is a good way to cut down on the number of toys you need to own and will give children the delight of a "new" toy. It is a good way to extend the life of play equipment too; most is sturdily built, but may only have a short lifespan before children outgrow it. Set up an exchange session with friends, or give toys to local play groups or nursery schools, to hospitals, children's libraries, or to charitable organizations.

Repair children's toys before buying new ones; for specialist repairs such as teddy bear or doll restoration, check your local telephone directory or ask at a local toy shop. Always use non-toxic **adhesives** and **paints**.

Thrift project
How to make a sock snake
- You will need several socks of the same size, preferably children's striped, cotton ones.
- Cut sections from the socks and sew them together, making one pointed for the tail, and keep another whole for the head.
- Stuff with old tights/pantyhose and sew up.
- Poke in the mouth and sew in a ribbon for the forked tongue. Sew on buttons for eyes.

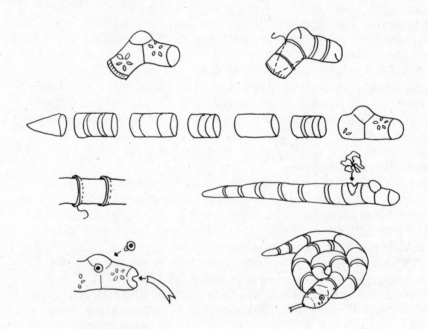

Thrift project
How to make a papier mâché shakers
- Cover a small round balloon with paper mâché (shredded newpaper soaked in flour and water paste – see p.98), leaving a hole for the filling and wooden handle.
- When the papier mâché is dry, burst the balloon with a pin, leaving the round shape.
- Fill this with dried peas or lentils, and attach a wooden stick – a wooden spoon handle is ideal. Paint and decorate.

How to make a papier mâché mask
- Cover a shallow cake tin or a plastic bowl with papier mâché.
- When the papier mâché is dry, cut out eye and nose holes, attach a piece of elastic to either side.
- Paint on eyebrows, lips and ears. Or make a wildlife mask.

TRASH see Solid waste

TUMBLER, COMPOST
Facts
Tumblers produce a **compost** from kitchen and **garden/backyard waste** much faster than the traditional compost heap and take up less space in a small garden. Mount the barrel on a steel frame to allow it to be rotated once a day. Try organic gardening organizations or appropriate technology groups for information on building your own low-cost composter (see Resources).

Reuse/Recycle

If you make your own tumbler from an old metal oil drum give it a rust-proof coating before use. Site the tumbler anywhere in the garden, but preferably in the sun, which will help the compost temperature to rise. Place a drip tray under the tumbler to catch the liquid **leachate** when the barrel is rotated, otherwise this concentrated juice can stain or burn the surrounding grass or stone. Dilute it – at least 20 parts to 1 part – and reuse as a liquid plant feed.

Fill the tumbler with compostible material – grass clippings, vegetable peelings, and other organic matter – commercial tumblers include full instructions. With the right mix compost is produced within weeks and is suitable for **mulch** or digging into the soil. **See also** Compost

---

TYPEWRITERS

Facts

Typewriters are sturdy machines that will last if properly maintained and they have a scrap value at the end of their life. It is the frequent replacement of ribbon cassettes that creates the waste. Every year, 26 million ribbon cassettes are discarded in the UK alone. Globally this wastage of metal and **plastic** cartridges is huge – and unnecessary. Many suppliers now offer a re-inking service for fabric ribbons, or will "remanufacture" or reload new ribbons into used plastic casings. A thriving industry for this exists in China and Japan, where most ribbons are made. Some of these are already made from recycled plastic – recovered plastics from telephone recycling go into complex mouldings such as printer ribbon cassettes.

Reuse

Get fabric ribbons reinked – this is cheaper than buying a new ribbon each time. Ribbons last for several return trips before they are too worn. And collect other types for recycling. Find out what happens to old typewriter ribbons in your workplace and exert pressure to change over to recyclables. Reduce the environmental impact of other typewriter equipment you buy. Many types of correcting fluid are manufactured from toxic solvents containing ozone-depleting substances; avoid all products containing 1-1-1 trichloroethane. Major brand names make non-toxic types.

Although computers are replacing many of the functions of a typewriter, **second-hand stores** take unwanted items or trade your machine in part-exchange for new equipment. Not-for-profit groups are always short of working typewriters. **See also** Office equipment

---

TYRES
Facts
Finding appropriate uses for discarded car tyres is a major environmental headache. The US discards 250 million a year and the UK 25 million. Recycling rates are increasing, but not fast enough to prevent tyres being illegally dumped or landfilled.

There used to be a thriving market for retreads (remoulds) in industrialized countries. But this practice has declined as manufacturers claim that tyres are being worn harder, making them unsuitable for retreading. This reprocessing gives them a new gripping surface and on a 35,000-mile tyre, the financial savings are 30-50%. Remoulding remains the most desirable environmental and economic option; it saves primary raw materials – mostly petroleum, **steel**, and synthetic fibres, and reduces the need for tyre disposal in **landfill** sites. Currently about one-fifth of the vehicle tyres in the US are retreads, while the Netherlands plans to use half their scrap tyres for remoulds and the rest for new technologies including "crumb rubber".

The largest component of a tyre is petroleum-based products – it takes half a barrel of crude **oil** (about 90 litres/20 gallons) to make just the synthetic **rubber** in a truck tyre. While tyres are a potential source of energy, mishandling them causes serious problems. A massive fire at a Canadian tyre dump in 1989 lead to 15 million tyres releasing a toxic black smoke. The potential for air pollution is immense; tyres smoulder for many years and each one can release 11 litres (2½ gallons) of **oil** into the ground.

Many landfill operators refuse to take tyres in any volume – within a landfill they absorb gases from decomposing waste, causing them to slowly rise to the surface, creating instability within the site. As a result, huge tyre dumps have developed while a solution to their disposal is sought. In Connecticut, US, a disused water-filled quarry is used for storing tyres (much more environonentally benign); tyres not sold to manufacturers for reuse are recycled by Goodwill Industries into rubber mats, and elsewhere as backing for carpets.

If reclaimed shredded rubber is incorporated into surfacing materials for roads, pavements, and children's playgrounds, the surfaces last up to five times longer. And at Gatwick and Heathrow (UK) airports a non-slip road surface has been made from pulverized tyres and tarmac. Another option is tyre-to-energy plants, already popular in the US. The first plant in Europe has opened in Wolverhampton in the UK. Using discarded vehicle tyres for dock and boat fenders is an established practice and in the US they have been used for building breakwaters and creating artificial fish reefs. They can also be pyrolized into fuel oil – a car tyre yields 4 litres (1 gallon) of oil of fuel oil and 450 cubic feet of gas, more than enough to heat a home for a day.

In developing countries, discarded tyres are valuable objects and their reuse is seen everywhere. Cut into strips they can be woven into door mats, chair seats, and in North Africa, Latin America, and Asia, the soles, heels and straps of shoes are made from tyres. According to Oxfam, shoes made from tyre grips last 5-10 times longer than mass-produced **plastic** shoes and sandals. Tyre material is also used for repairs. Small workshops in Morocco fashion water carriers out of old car tyres and other objects include mats for cars, hinges for gates, rubber cord for tethering animals, bags, and seating.

Reuse/Recycle

Cut waste by buying long-life tyres. Extend their wear through regular maintenance and check tyre pressure frequently. Consider buying retreads if available, or use them as your spare tyre. If they cannot be retreaded, a few tyres may be needed on farms for holding down plastic sheeting, or give them to adventure playgrounds. Suspended on a metal chain or rope they make excellent swings. Tyres filled with soil make ideal plant holders. Disguise them by painting or covering with trailing plants. Alternatively cut them up, turn inside out, and fill with soil, or use the rubber for protective edging in the garden around the base of trees or shrubs so that you don't damage them when mowing grass.

Recycle

Find out whether a local service station or recycling centre will take old tyres back for reprocessing. If not, dispose of them at your local civic amenity sites.

U

UNBLEACHED PRODUCTS
Facts
Bright white **paper** may look clean and inviting, but producing it from
brown wood pulp is a dirty and deadly business. Chlorine bleaching
creates poisonous byproducts, including **dioxin** and organochlorines,
which cause substantial water pollution around pulp mills. Oxygen
bleaching is less hazardous; many manufacturers have adopted this
method following consumer pressure for change. Others leave
products unbleached. Bleaching is not necessary for many products –
coffee filters, **nappies/diapers**, and **toilet paper**, to name three. The
Canadian Reach for the Unbleached campaign is working to
deprogramme beliefs that white is cleaner and therefore better.
Although Sweden has used unbleached, or chlorine-free, products
since 1987, it still produces chlorine-bleached pulp for export to the UK.
Reuse
Instead of using disposable coffee filters, even the unbleached ones,
buy a reusable cotton filter, or use a different method of making coffee.
Write to packaging manufacturers asking them to switch to safer
methods, or ask why it is really necessary to bleach some packaging –
for example, cereal boxes. Instead of paper handkerchiefs, use
washable cotton ones.
   Buy unbleached, recycled paper products and if bright white paper is
necessary for your office stationery purchase oxygen or hydrogen
peroxide treated paper only.
Recycle
Unbleached products can be recycled in the same way as other paper.
Put disposable coffee filters into worm bins. **See also** Vermiculture

UPHOLSTERY
Facts
The furniture industry is a major user of **plastic foam** fillings, which
can contain CFC-related products. Legislation controlling the use of
flammable foams has benefitted the textile reprocessing trade as it has
increased demand for upholstery fillings from reclaimed fabrics.

Mattresses, chairs, and car interiors frequently contain such materials. The trend to go back to using natural products means that cotton, coir, and wool fibres are widely available.

Reuse/Repair/Recycle

Replacing fabric coverings and stuffing is usually worthwhile if furniture is generally in good condition. Leaving repairs for another few months is not a good idea; by then reupholstering may have turned into a major job. Many antique pieces are extremely sturdy; restoring them in this way gives years of additional use, although it can be expensive, depending on the work that needs to be done and the availability of materials. Horsehair was once a popular stuffing material, for this items now need to be taken to a professional upholsterer for repair. Some refurbishment workshops offer skills training to the long-term unemployed and carry out all sorts of upholstery work.

V

VACUUM CLEANERS
Facts

Low-voltage (12V) appliances are available, but most are of inferior quality and are inefficient. However further technological developments will lead to improvements, and models are available, including a car-type vacuum cleaner and a cordless, rechargeable full-size unit, which are comparable to normal mains vacuum cleaners for room-at-a-time cleaning.

A cheaper alternative is to buy a reconditioned vacuum cleaner from a reputable dealer. These second-hand goods need not be of inferior quality, provided you keep them well maintained. Alternatively buy a mechanical carpet sweeper. Vacuum dust can be composted, although some sources warn that modern appliances may use lead **alloys**, which could add **lead** particles to your soil.

VEGETABLE WASTES AND PEELINGS see Organic waste

VEHICLE RECYCLING
Facts

Worldwide there are nearly 400 million **cars**, in addition to all the other types of motor vehicles. Converting raw materials into materials for car manufacture is energy-intensive; 11 gigajoules in Japan is average, while the US uses a massive 32. In use, vehicles pollute, with 98% of transport energy coming from non-renewable resources, including petroleum, and their eventual disposal creates large volumes of waste.

In 1987, the US vehicle industry consumed (as a proportion of the total US consumption) 74% of natural **rubber**, 54% of **lead**, 46% of synthetic rubber, 43% of **iron**, 39% of platinum, 16% of **aluminium**, 15% of **steel**, and 0.3% of cotton. Of the 15.5 million tonnes, all were finite resources except for the natural rubber and cotton.

At the end of its life, an old vehicle contains a wide range of valuable materials, but until recently most were only broken up for their metal content. But now dismantling and recovery plants covering all the recyclable materials are being planned throughout Europe. There is a long tradition of reclaiming scrap metal – primarily iron and steel – from cars, but the proportions of these are declining as **plastic** is substituted. It is technically possible to return approximately 75% of materials back into the vehicle production system and car manufacturers are already promoting their products as "80% recyclable". A German manufacturer is developing a research centre to investigate the best practicable means of disassembling vehicles for recycling. Others are researching ways of making plastic components more readily recyclable. **See also** Cars

---

VERMICULTURE
Facts
Letting worms compost your kitchen food scraps is an easy way of recycling organic waste, as well as producing a rich, fertile soil conditioner for your garden/backyard. Worms are the earth's natural recyclers, dragging dead and dying organic matter down into the soil and digesting it; the worm cast is the compost.

Special worms – variously known as redworms, tiger worms, or brandlings (*Eisenia Foetida* and *Eisenia Andrei*) are used in commercial worm composting projects. They do occur naturally in **compost** heaps and are the best species for composting organic matter rapidly and efficiently. Pilot and large-scale vermiculture projects are under way in many countries, including North America, the UK, and Germany. Being a new technology it is meeting with problems that hinder its development. In Sacramento, California, one worm composting company is fighting to change the rules that require it to obtain the same type of permit as is normally required for siting a **landfill**.

Reuse
Complete worm composting kits, including the worms, are available (see Resources) or build your own worm box out of discarded materials (see **Thrift project**). A bin with a capacity of 90 litres will cater for the waste from a family of four. Contact organic growing organizations (see Resources) for advice. You can buy the composting worms from specialist stockists, or from stores selling fishing bait. The bedding for the worms – sedge peat, leafmould, or shredded **newspaper** – must be

kept damp for the worms to thrive. Add food regularly by burying it in the top layers of the bedding.

Worms eat most types of kitchen waste – peelings, tea bags, coffee grounds (plus filter papers), vegetable waste, cooked waste scraps, egg shells (good for stopping the contents becoming too acidic if you are putting a lot of citrus skins into the bin) and even shredded paper. But to avoid smells and potential problems with rodents, do not include meat or fatty dairy foods like cheese. Generally, the recycling process is virtually odour-free, and worm bins in kitchens are not uncommon. If you have a problem with fruit flies, a tested remedy is to lightly spray vinegar over the surface of the compost – the smell is offputting to flies, but don't use too much otherwise the bin might get too acidic, or put strips of fabric soaked in peppermint or citrus essential oils on the surface of the compost.

In addition to the worm compost, a concentrated liquid feed is produced from the decaying vegetable matter. Some commercial worm bins are designed to trap this, allowing you to drain the liquid from a small tap. Diluted with water, it makes a nutritious plant food. A small bin yields compost in 2-3 months; after removing this, you are ready to start again, reusing a few handfuls of the compost as bedding for the worms. They reproduce quickly in the right conditions, so you shouldn't need to buy more once you've started. **See also** Compost, Organic Waste

Thrift project
How to make a worm bin
- Construct a shallow wooden box (30cm/1ft deep, 60cm/2ft wide, 90cm/3ft long), with a tightly fitting lid, from untreated plywood, or convert an old cupboard or packaging crate.
- Drill drainage holes in the bottom and put in a layer of sand to help retain moisture.
- Fill with damp leaves and shredded moist newspaper. Bury some food wastes (fruit and vegetable peelings, tea bags, etc) in this bedding.
- Add 450g (15oz) of red worms and wait a few weeks to let them settle down before adding more food.
- After 3-6 months start harvesting your compost. In colder weather it is best to insulate the bin with old sacking, newspaper, or straw.

VIDEOS AND VIDEO CASSETTES

The best way of maximizing the variety of materials that make up such equipment is to keep it going until it is beyond repair. Upgrading to the next model is rarely necessary, so ignore sales pressure to do this. If you hire videos and they break down, your service contract will probably cover repair or replacement. Reconditioned videos are available in **second-hand stores**.

The **plastic** casings used for cassettes frequently contain a mixture of recycled plastic recovered from **telephones**, coat hangers, or plastic scrap. Household recycling of broken videos is not recommended unless you are mechanically minded, and can dismantle equipment for spare parts.

WALLPAPERS AND COVERINGS

Facts
Of all the different types of wallcoverings, vinyl-based wallpapers create
the biggest impact on the environment; their production waste cannot
be burned due to hazards from toxic vapours. A company in Germany is
pioneering reuse by separating the vinyl from the rest of the **paper**; the
recovered paper is then processed into a new wallpaper base.
Thousands of tonnes of vinyl waste from the UK is already transported
by rail to Germany for treatment. All wallpaper **adhesives** are
contaminants in recycling processes. Recycled wallpaper is available.

Reuse
Try experimenting with alternative wall coverings. Although vinyl
wallpaper is tough and easy to clean, other materials, based on natural
fibres (such as hessian, **cork**, and textiles) can be equally durable. For
example, hessian from plant fibres is often used by professional
decorators as a foundation for **paint**. Alternatively, use **tiles** and low-
emission paint, or use techniques such as rag rolling or stencilling.

Keep surplus scraps of wallpaper for repairs, or line drawers and
cupboards with it. If you have left-over rolls, see if the retailer will
accept them back, or give them to a **charity store** for resale. Unwanted
wallpaper sample books are usually thrown away at the end of the
season, yet wallpaper is always welcome for art projects at children's
playgroups, primary schools, or children's **scrapstores**. Make a
waterproof cover for a cookery book from spare sheets (see **Books**).

Recycle
Once wallpaper has been used it cannot be recycled into new products.
Wallpaper paste and adhesive backings contaminate the recycling
process. Dispose of it in the **dustbin/garbage bin**. Do not put vinyl-
backed paper on bonfires – it releases toxic gases.

WASHING MACHINES
Facts
These white goods are largely made of **steel**, a valuable scrap metal. Its use in steel-making gives energy savings of up to 76%. But even if disposing of washing machines is relatively easy, the real impacts come from the amount of energy they take to manufacture and the amount they consume in normal use. In Europe major manufacturers claim their washing machines are "environment-friendly", but under a proposed European Community directive on eco-labelling, most would fail to reach the minimum standard for water and energy use. Washing machines consume about 12% of all water used in the home. Energy efficiency labelling is already in use in the US and in Australia.
Reuse/Repair/Recycle
From a financial point of view, if your current machine is in good working order, it is probably not worth switching models as it will take several years to recover the cost from reduced fuel bills. Instead maximize energy use by only washing when you can make up a full load. Use lower temperatures; hot washes are not necessary for many fabrics, and dry clothes outside rather than using the tumble drier.

Trade in an unwanted machine or take it to a **second-hand store** or refurbishment workshop for resale. Reconditioned machines will not be as energy-efficient as some new machines, so consider this before buying. If your washing machine breaks down, find out if it can be repaired before discarding it. In 1989, a survey of UK scrapheaps revealed that one-quarter of all washing machines had no obvious fault, while a further quarter could have been repaired cheaply and quickly.
See also Detergents

WASTE DISPOSAL UNITS
Facts
These units are marketed as convenience items; a garbage grinder is built into a double sink to grind and flush food waste into the sewerage system. Chemical treatments are sometimes added and there is no recycling. Waste disposal units are a standard fixture in many new homes in Australia, but in Germany and the Netherlands their use is frowned upon. In Ontario, Canada, the city of Peterborough bans the sale and operation of all sink garbage grinders in industrial,

commercial, and residential buildings. To encourage recycling, the city has cut back on the number of garbage containers it collects from each household; anticipating problems with people using waste grinders to dispose of food waste, and the subsequent need for increased expenditure in sewage treatment facilities, the city passed legislation in January 1991. Grinders installed before that date are not affected.

Reuse/Recycle
Waste disposal units create an additional burden on our already overloaded **sewage** systems. Avoid using them. Keep suitable organic food waste for the **compost** heap; or dig a compost trench or set up a worm bin (see **Vermiculture**) in your garden.

WASTE PAPER
Facts
This commodity has been used as a primary fibre in paper-making for more than a century; today it is an increasingly important resource. Yet its full potential is hampered by the relatively low level of recycling in many countries. The UK, for example, recovers just 34% of its waste **paper**, which is way behind other European countries.

Forecasts of the paperless office have proved a myth. In the US it is calculated that enough computer paper is spewed out each day to encircle the world 40 times. Every person in the UK annually accounts for 130kg (286lb) of paper and **cardboard** – about two trees worth! Much of this ends up in the **dustbin/garbage bin** – 30% of the contents of an average bin will be discarded paper and cardboard.

Recycling paper is vital because the more paper we produce from virgin pulp, the more trees we cut down. And at present, 131 million trees are used every year. Recycling waste paper reduces industrial water use by 58%, energy use by 40%, air pollution by 74%, and water pollution by 35%. Recycling also helps reduce dependence on imported goods and raw materials. In the UK, for example, an increased rate of recycling would contribute an estimated £800 million to the balance of payments. Recycling a tonne of paper saves 2, 750 k Wh – or enough electricity to feed a 100 W lightbulb 24 hours a day for three years. Waste paper can also be used to make plasterboard or fire-resistant insulation material. Other destinations are cardboard, pulp packaging and even animal bedding, reducing the need for straw.

Reuse/Recycle

The biggest contribution individuals can make is to buy recycled paper products, both at home and at work. This helps create a demand for recycled paper, bringing benefits in terms of quality and price. Put pressure on your workplace to establish a workplace recycling scheme, particularly for high-grade office paper. (Seek advice on paper grading systems.)

When collecting waste paper, find out where you can take it, or who will collect it, before the pile grows too high. Your local authority may have a collection point at a civic amenity site, or at a recycling centre. Some voluntary groups run smaller collections, but can be hard hit when waste prices fluctuate. For large quantities, try waste merchants. **See also** Office waste paper, Paper

Use of waste paper in making new board and paper, 1990

Denmark	69%
Germany	43%
Netherlands	68%
Portugal	43%
Spain	62%
Italy	42%
UK	57%
Belgium	24%
France	44%

WATER HEATERS see Central heating, Solar power

WATER, POLLUTION OF
Facts
Water is an essential part of many manufacturing processes. Although many companies cut costs by recycling water, vast quantities are still wasted by inefficient practices in the workplace and in the home.

Water quality is declining rapidly in many countries. Reducing our use of hazardous substances, including pesticides and fertilizers on agricultural land, is vital to protect existing water supplies from land run-off. Even the disposal of common household items, for example **batteries**, has a substantial impact. Leaking **landfills** pose a great threat to underground water supplies. Another major source of water pollution is the presence of organic materials such as **sewage** and farm waste. Safe treatment processes using bacteria exist and the end result can be a valuable soil conditioner. **See** Greywater systems

WHITE GOODS
Facts
This term applies to **refrigerators, freezers, washing machines**, and **cookers/stoves**. All of them are a major source of **steel** scrap, yet their recycling can have a negative impact upon the environment. Motors and compressors in older electrical appliances have parts likely to contain PCBs. As appliances are crushed and shredded for scrap, PCBs escape into the environment. These are toxic and are not biodegradable, causing serious long-term ground and water pollution. They are categorized as hazardous waste and their use was banned in the US in 1979. The safe solution is to remove machine parts before appliances are sent for scrap. Reputable scrap dealers will do this and will provide advice to people dismantling equipment. CFCs in the coolant and insulation in fridges and freezers must be recovered for safe disposal or reprocessing before these items are crushed.

Reuse
Too many quality appliances are discarded or upgraded for new models before the end of their useful life. If your fridge or cooker/stove is still in good working condition, consider whether you really do need to change it. Could you do without that latest gadget on newer models? Would it work more efficiently if you had it reconditioned.

If you do need to change appliances, ask whether the retailer will trade-in old for new equipment. This way you do not have the problem of disposing of a heavy item, and it will probably be sold to a dealer for reconditioning or scrap. Donations of working equipment are always needed by charities dealing with the needy or homeless. Nearly every **second-hand store** accepts and sells such products. Older appliances are not as energy-efficient as many new models on sale – consider this before buying; an older appliance may not be such a bargain.

Repair

Unfortunately too many products are now designed with "built-in obsolescence". The lack of essential spare parts means that appliances are discarded in relatively good condition. Even when repairable, some people discard rather than repair. Yet simple repairs are often all that is needed to restore an appliance to working condition. Manufacturers should be able to supply spare parts; don't attempt repairs unless you know what you are doing. Seek professional help.

Recycle

Take items to recycling centres, but check that processing for scrap is undertaken in a responsible manner.

WINDOW FRAMES

Facts

Unless the frames are wooden and rotten, there is usually a demand for items recovered from building restoration work; they can be used as replacement frames or sold to **salvage** and scrap yards. Pure **aluminium** frames fetch a high scrap price; the metal is easily recycled, with the benefit of a 95% energy saving over the cost of making new aluminium sheet metal. **Steel** is always wanted at scrap yards. **PVC** window frames, if recycled, can be made into pipes, flooring, or garden furniture. In the US and parts of Europe, salvage is lucrative as home alterations create an endless source of materials.

Reuse

Make a cheap cold frame for raising garden plants from a discarded window frame. If you are replacing a window frame, check the wood for rot. Do not buy tropical hardwoods to replace or repair splintered frames – use other timbers. The joinery trade remains the biggest user of tropical timber and most hardwood window frames are replacements put in by homeowners, not builders. If you buy these, you are directly supporting companies involved in rainforest destruction.

Recycle

Take unwanted metal frames to **scrap merchants**, salvage centres, or second-hand dealers. Flat **glass** from frames should not be put in a **bottle bank** – this type of glass is made from different materials and is often specially strengthened. It will contaminate the bottle recycling process. **See also** PVC

WOOD
Facts
Wood is the basic raw material for common items including **paper**, newsprint, furniture, and **building materials**. Worldwide, over 2500 million people depend on wood for their daily needs. Trees are a renewable resource, but current uses are depleting, rather than sustaining, this resource base. Forestry practices need to be sustainable; forests play a crucial role in the planetary recycling of carbon, nitrogen and oxygen, the essential elements of life, as well as being diverse ecological habitats for an array of wildlife.

In industrialized countries, wood is still a wasted resource. Urban wood waste accounts for about 10% of municipal solid waste in North America. Several cities, including Toronto, Canada, plan to ban the disposal of such wood in **landfills**. Instead, wood processing and recycling facilities are being set up to convert wood into particle board, roofing felt, animal bedding, **mulch**, and road base. Wood bark can be used as the fuel for powering these processing plants. In Ontario government studies demonstrate that 52% of wood waste gets re-utilized – either through direct reuse, recycling, or by recovering the energy or organic component of the wood. However there is a problem with bulky wood pallets, only one in every 33 gets reused or recycled.

Even the wood from dead Christmas trees is recyclable – but a much better option is to buy a living tree to plant outside after the festive season. Failing that a power shredder quickly reduces a tree into reusable wood chips, or cut the wood into firewood. Wood-burning stoves are the cleanest and most efficient way of burning seasoned wood; at the right temperature pollutants are kept to a minimum, and energy can be reclaimed for heating and cooking.

Reuse/Recycle
Think of new ways of reusing wood around your home: use warped shelving or doors for storage or work surfaces in the garage; make a trellis for climbing garden plants from longer pieces of wood or poles; build a wooden frame for your **compost** heap, make a coat or tool rack, and use wood to make simple chidren's **toys**.

Never buy tropical timbers. Friends of the Earth UK (see Resources) publishes a Good Wood Guide and will advise on suitable alternatives. Burning usable wood on a **bonfire** as a means of disposing of it is not recycling. If you cannot use it, is there a local environmental or wildlife group that could use reclaimed wood for bird or bat boxes, or fencing? Or perhaps a youth training or refurbishment workshop might have some use for it?

Repair

With care, high-quality wooden furniture and fittings will last a lifetime. Tackle simple repairs at home with the right tools and wherever possible, use non-toxic adhesives. Hire power **tools** to strip old **paint** off woodwork and restore by staining the wood or revarnishing (see Resources for materials based on natural resins rather than chemicals).

Recycle

Never put old painted wood (the paint might contain **lead**) or wood treated with preservatives on a fire – air pollution is a potential hazard. If the wood is good quality, see if a second-hand merchant or **salvage** yard wants it. If not, take it to a recycling centre or civic amenity site.

Borrow or hire a chipper to make a woody **mulch** from garden waste, and **compost** left-over sawdust. **See also** Timber

---

WOOD PULP

Facts

Wood pulp is the basic raw material for the paper industry. Canada, Sweden, and Finland are the world's largest exporters, but the huge profits are not made without equivalent costs to the environment. Pulping processes separate useful fibres from the impurities, and processing creates toxic effluents. The health of workers at chemical pulping mills is often at risk. An average-sized bleach pulpmill, with a daily production of about 1000 tonnes of pulp, releases between 20 and 50 tonnes of chlorinated compounds each day. Sulphur dioxide, responsible for "acid rain", is released by pulping processes. The sulphite process (boiling wood chips in an acid solution) releases 5kg (11lb) of sulphur dioxide into the atmosphere for every tonne of pulp produced. When we indiscriminately use disposable **paper** products, we need to remember these hidden impacts.

Trees only contain about 50% cellulose, the rest is lignin, aromatic oils, and resins. Pulp is made by separating out cellulose fibres. Different trees produce different pulps, for example, deciduous hardwood trees have short fibres, producing a smooth paper for high-quality printing. Other fibrous materials also produce pulp; hemp, cotton rags, and straw – although the lower cellulose content means that processing produces relatively large amounts of effluent. Yet straw is often a waste product, available in large quantities. In the UK the paper industry is conducting pilot studies for straw-based manufacturing plants.

Besides paper, wood pulp is used to make **cellophane** and textiles such as rayon. But it is the growing worldwide demand for paper that is responsible for environmental devastation in Canada, where the cost of wood is 60% lower than Sweden. Almost 80% of Canadian pulp and paper products are exported.

Reuse/Recycling
Cutting paper wastage, and thus demand, is crucial. "Millbroke" and high-quality postconsumer waste can be used as a direct substitute for pulp in the paper-making process. Starting up an office collection scheme is one way of returning waste for recycling. The paper must be free from **plastics** or **laminates**. Contact a paper collector before you start, some also offer shredding services for confidential documents. And get your workplace to buy recycled paper goods.

WOOL AND WOOLLEN GOODS
Facts
As a natural fibre wool is easy to reuse or recycle into other woollen products. Yet every year between 3 and 5% of the UK's domestic rubbish consists of textiles – knitwear and woollen goods make up a significant part of this waste despite a good market for reclaimed items.

Recycling wool helps cut the environmental impact arising from its original production. Processing a tonne of wool from the fleece to the finished product uses as much as 200,000 litres of water. 70% of the world's wool comes from Australia and New Zealand, where sheep-rearing practices are heavily dependent on chemicals for pest control. After shearing, fleeces are usually treated with mothproofing chemicals, including permethrin. Such toxic substances are harmful to wildlife; as a result the EC is introducing stricter controls on the release of effluent from January 1993. As much as 50,000 litres of waste liquid is produced for each tonne of treated wool. And chemical **dyes** and treatments add a further pollution burden.

After such intensive processing, keeping wool in circulation is environmentally desirable. At textile sorting plants such as Oxfam's Wastesaver in the UK, woollen garments are graded as suitable for blending with new wool to produce a moderately priced fabric, or lower grades are processed into an upholstery stuffing for chairs and mattresses.

Reuse/Repair

If you want to avoid using heavily processed wool, unbleached and undyed wool is available from some mills. Reuse wool by unravelling old jumpers for reknitting. Woollen fibres are long and unless the original wool was matted or felted they are fine for making jumpers, soft **toys**, or blanket squares. When you have enough squares, sew the edges together into a small blanket that could also be used as a shawl or into a full-sized blanket. Major aid and development charities always need wool squares and blankets for their work with refugees or the dispossessed.

Repair

Keep scraps of wool left over after knitting to mend holes, or unravel an old wool garment – **jumble sales** are a cheap source – for repair wool.

Recycle

Take all woollen garments in good condition to **charity stores** for resale, give to groups working with the needy or homeless and take those past repair to rag banks operated by the Salvation Army, Goodwill, and similar charities.

WRAPPING PAPER

Facts

All sorts of **paper** items end up as wrapping paper – from yesterday's newspaper for the fish and chips to elaborate metal foils used in gift **packaging**. Some are essential uses, others are just frivolous. The huge pile of discarded wrapping paper at Christmas is a yearly reminder of just how much we do waste. The ultimate reusable packaging, a surfactant "paper" made of liquid soap and dried on glass sheets is being used by a small UK company for packaging some of its toiletries. Reuse is a theme for another small company which collects old maps and converts them into recycled wrapping paper and stationery.

Reuse

The best way of solving the problem of what to do with wrapping paper is not to accumulate it in the first place. Reuse the obvious – waxed papers in cereal boxes are ideal for sandwiches, brown parcel paper is strong enough for several trips, and butter or margarine wrappers are useful for greasing cake tins. If you have paper bags, reuse them. Brown bags usually contain recycled paper, but that doesn't mean that they cannot be recycled again. Give unwanted bags or large amounts of paper (tissue paper, etc.) to local market traders or jumble sales.

Consider ways of giving presents without using disposable wrappings, or use the wrapping as part of the gift. Buy colourful fabric remnants and make into simple tray or table cloths, or napkins. Or wrap gifts in a silk scarf or ethnic prints, using ribbon or colourful shoe laces to fasten. The paper from colour magazines is ideal for reusing this way. Keeping Christmas paper for next year is a good idea – iron crumpled pieces or give to children for craft projects.

WRITING PAPER see Paper

Z

ZINC
Facts

Zinc is a metal derived from metallic ores mined throughout the world, including Australia, Canada, and the US. Zinc smelting is carried out in most industrialized countries – its production is no more hazardous than other metals. Zinc is commonly used to manufacture a number of alloys – for example, combined with **copper** it makes brass.

Zinc is used throughout the building trade as an acceptable substitute for **lead** because it has a low toxicity in normal use. Unlike many metals it doesn't rust, making it widely used as a roofing material and as a protective covering for **iron** and **steel**. It is also a component in metal-priming paints, in fungicide **wood** treatments, and is found in low-energy zinc-carbon batteries.

Reuse

Zinc is valuable as non-ferrous scrap and is widely recycled within the metal industry. But since it is usually found in combination with other metals, its reuse depends on these products. Contact a scrap dealer if you have reasonable quantities from restoration work – for example roof replacement. Otherwise **salvage** yards, "rag and bone" collectors or "totters" might take the odd item from you.

If you want to reuse zinc sheeting by painting it, you must leave the metal to weather, otherwise the paint will flake. And when sanding down paintwork primed with zinc metal primer, use a face mask or avoid breathing in any particles. **See** Batteries

ZIPS
Facts

The humble zip fastener was invented in 1893 and is now found in use in all kinds of equipment, from **clothing** to the giant bags used for making sileage from farm wastes. Metal zips are generally stronger than the plastic variety, but both types are hardwearing.

Reuse

Remove zips for reuse from any clothing destined for the **rag** bank. Either keep for replacing faulty or broken zips in other clothes, or give

to friends, **jumble sales**, repair workshops, or **charity stores**.
Repair
Broken zips are fiddly to replace, even with a sewing machine.
Professional repairs are undertaken at many stores – tailors,
drycleaners, and shoe repair outlets. But an emergency repair is
possible where the zip runner has broken free of the teeth on one side.

Thrift project
How to repair a zip
- Pull the runner to the bottom of the zip. Cut into the zip tape between
the two teeth about 6 mm (¼ in) above the runner on the broken side.
- Work the teeth above the cut into the runner. Pull the runner up over
the cut and oversew across the zip to create a new bottom stop.

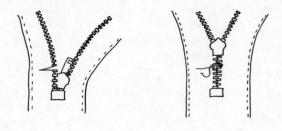

RESOURCES

This is a small selection of organizations, suppliers and contacts

Alcan Aluminium Can Recycling
Latchford Locks Office
Warrington
Cheshire WA4 1NP
Tel. 0925 35314
(Operates buy-back centres and collection facilities. Freephone: 0800 262465)

Aluminium Can Recycling Association (ACRA)
Suite 308
Imex House
52 Blucher St
Birmingham B1 1QU
Tel. 021 633 4656
(Educational and publicity material, advises on "cash for cans" schemes)

Aluminium Foil Recycling Campaign
38-42 High Street
Bidford-on-Avon
Warwickshire B50 4AA

Association of Environment-Conscious Builders
Windlake House
The Pump Field, Coaley
Glos. GL11 5DX
Tel. 0453 890757
(Promotes sustainable building practices and materials use)

British Glass
Northumberland House
Sheffield
Yorks. S10 2UA
Tel. 0742 686201
(Co-ordinates UK bottle bank scheme)

British Paper & Board Industry Federation Ltd
Papermakers House
Rivenhall Rd
Swindon SN5 7BE

British Plastics Federation
5 Belgrave Square
London SW1X 8PQ
Tel. 071 235 9483

British Waste Paper Association
Station Rd
Aldershot
Hants. GU11 1BQ
Tel. 0252 344454
(Supplies list of waste paper merchants and advises on collections)

Centre for Alternative Technology
Machynlleth
Powys SY20 9AZ
Tel. 0654 702400
(Promotes sustainable technologies - wind, water, solar, energy conservation, and recycling. Practical expertise in renewable energy, energy conservation, organic growing, and ecological building. Information service, training, mail-order supplies)

Charities Aid Foundation
48 Pembury Rd
Tonbridge
Kent, TN9 2JD
Tel. 0732 771333
(Publishes directory listing materials that charities collect)

Community Recycling Network (CRN)
10-12 Picton St
Montpelier
Bristol BS6 5QA
Tel. 0272 420142
(Promotes good practice in community recycling)

Department of Trade and Industry - environmental helpline for free advice on issues affecting businesses.
Tel. 0800 858794

Eco-House
Leicester Ecology Trust
Parkfield
Western Park, Hinckley Rd
Leicester LE3 6HX
Tel. 0533 856675
(Demonstration house and garden/information centre)

Ecological Design Association (EDA)
20 High St
Stroud
Glos. GL5 1AS
Tel. 0453 765575
(Leading organization for architects and designers)

Friends of the Earth (UK)
26-8 Underwood St
London N1 7JD
Tel. 071 490 1555

Furniture Recycling Network
c/o SOFA, Pilot House
41 King St
Leicester LE1 6RN
Tel. 0533 545283
(Co-ordinating body for furniture recycling)

Greenpeace UK
Greenpeace House
Canonbury Villas
London N1 2HB
Tel. 071 354 5100

Henry Doubleday Research Organisation (HDRA) National Centre for Organic Gardening Ryton Organic Gardens Ryton-on-Dunsmore Coventry CV8 3LG Tel. 0203 303517 (Promotes all aspects of organic horticulture and agriculture. Demonstration gardens, information service, training courses, and extensive mail-order service)

Intermediate Technology Development Group Myson House Railway Terrace Rugby CV21 3HT Tel. 0788 560631 (International development agency working with rural communities in developing countries)

National Recycling Forum (NRF) 6-8 Great George St Leeds LS1 3DW Tel. 0532 431562 (Provides national focus for development of recycling and waste minimization)

Oxfam Wastesaver Unit 4-6, Ringway Industrial Estate, Beck Rd Huddersfield HG1 5DG (Textile reclamation plant)

Permaculture Association PO Box 1 Buckfastleigh Devon TQ11 OLH

RECOUP 9 Metro Centre Welbeck Way Shrewsbury Avenue Woodston

Peterborough PE2 7WH Tel. 0733 390021 (Not-for-profit organization to develop plastic bottle recycling schemes)

Save-a-Can PO Box 18 Ebbw Vale Gwent NP3 6YL Tel. 0495 350818 (Information on can recycling sites)

Soil Association Organic Food and Farming Centre 86 Colston St Bristol BS1 5BB Tel. 0272 290661 (Promotes organic agriculture, acts as consumer watchdog on food quality)

Steel Can Recycling Information Bureau 69 Monmouth St London WC2H 9DG (Can recycling information and free magnets. 24-hour hotline: 071 379 1306)

SWAP Recycling PO Box 19 6-8 Great George St Leeds LS1 6TF Tel. 0532 438777 (Promotes best environmental practice in resource use, etc.)

Tidy Britain Group The Pier Wigan WN3 4EX Tel. 0942 824620 (Campaigns for a litter-free Britain)

Tools for Self Reliance Netley Marsh Southampton SO4 2GY Tel. 0703 869697 (Collects unwanted tools

for developing countries)

Warren Spring Laboratory Recycling Advisory Unit Gunnels Wood Rd Stevenage Herts SG1 2BX (Technical research and information. Run DTI's Environmental Helpline Tel. 0800 585794)

Warmer Campaign 83 Mount Ephraim Tunbridge Wells Kent TN4 8BS Tel. 0892 524626 (Encourages recycling of materials and energy from post-consumer waste. Publishes WARMER bulletin)

Waste Exchange Services 70 Brunswick St Stockton-on-Tees Cleveland TW18 1TG (Industrial recycling consultancy, finding use for surplus products, design of recycling facilities)

Waste Watch 68 Grafton Way London W1P 5LE Tel. 071 383 3320 (Promotes and supports action on waste reduction, reuse and recycling) WASTELINE Tel. 071 388 4277

Women's Environmental Network (WEN) Aberdeen Studios 22 Highbury Grove London N5 2EA Tel. 071 354 8823 (Not-for-profit organization empowering and educating women)

CONTACTS AND SUPPLIERS

Please note that the following list of suppliers and products does not imply endorsement by the author or publisher.

Mail-order services

Centre for Alternative Technology (see p.278)

The Green Store
Freepost
Bath
Avon BA1 2XF

World of Difference
London Ecology Centre
45 Shelton St
London WC2H 9HJ

Traidcraft
Kingsway
Gateshead
Tyne and Wear NE11 ONE
(Promotes fair trade in developing world)

Many environmental groups raise funds through selling goods with a message: Friends of the Earth, Greenpeace, Oxfam, Whale and Dolphin Society, Women's Environmental Movement

Bags

Bootstrap Bags
115 Somerset Rd
Handsworth
Birmingham B20 2JF
(Handmade bags from reclaimed fabrics)

Baths

Renubath Service
22B Dyer St Cirencester
Glos. GL7 5ET
(Colouring processes and renovations for cast-iron baths)

Boots and shoes

Dunlop Footwear Ltd
Winsford
Cheshire CW7 3QF
Tel. 0606 592041
(PVC Wellington boot recycling scheme)

Vegetarian Shoes
36 Gardner St
Brighton BN1 1UN
(Shop and mail-order service for leather-free shoes)

Building materials

Architectural Salvage Index
Hutton and Rostron
Netley House
Gomshall, Guildford
Surrey
(Trade information service for salvaged materials)

Salvo 93/4 Directory
PO Box 1295
Bath
Avon BA1 3TJ
Tel. 0225 445387
(Architectural salvage directory)

Constructive Individuals
Design and Training for Self Build
58A Arbour Square
London E1 OPS

Community Self Build Agency
18 Northampton Square
London EC1V OAJ

Panpro Ltd
Deeping St Nicholas
Spalding
Lincolnshire PE11 3HL
(Manufacturers of Compakboard)

James Muir
Atellus Ltd
Pack House, Marlour Rd
Maidenhead

Berkshire SL6
(Supplier of woodwool insulation boards)

Carpets

Crucial Trading Ltd
PO Box 689
London W2 4BX
(Natural floor coverings)

Charity collections

Charities Aid Foundation
48 Pembury Rd Tonbridge
Kent TN9 2JD
(Directory listing 45 items needed by charities)

Clothing/rags

Salvation Army (UK)
101 Queen Victoria St
London EC4P 4EP
(Reuses and recycles all types of clothing and operates rag banks)

Oxfam stores collect second-hand clothes for resale. Look in the telephone directory.

Oxfam Wastesaver
Unit 4-6
Ringway Industrial Estate
Huddersfield
W.Yorks. HD1 5DG
(Recycles and reprocesses unsold textiles from Oxfam stores, reusable clothing is sent to developing countries)

Natural Fact
30-40 Elcho St
London SW11 4AU
(Undyed and unbleached new cotton clothing)

Evergreen
Albert Mills
Batley Carr Dewsbury
WF13 2HE
(Sells recycled woollen fibres and clothes)

Scrap Scrap
Unit D4
Maw's Craft Centre
Ferry Rd, Jackfield
Shropshire TF8 7LS
(Reuses material to make
new clothes)

Compost products
Check Yellow Pages and
gardening centres for
products and equipment.

Henry Doubleday Research
Association
National Centre for
Organic Gardening
Ryton-on-Dunsmore
Coventry CV8 3LG
(Mail-order catalogue)

Blackwall Products
Unit 4
Riverside Industrial Estate
150 River Way
London SE10 OBH
(Compost tumblers, water
butts, water-saving pipes)

Bio-Composter Containers
Plastopan Ltd
17 Museum St, Ipswich
Suffolk IP1 1HE
(Container enables organic
material to be collected
separately)

Green Cone Ltd
Suite One
Saunderton Carriage House
Wycombe Rd, Saunderton
High Wycombe
Bucks HP14 4HX
(Takes all kitchen food
waste)

Simplefit Ltd
Garden Products Division
Brokenford Lane
Totton, Southampton
Hants SO4 4DY
(Manufactures range of
compost-makers)

Compost toilets
Swedal (UK) Ltd
PO Box 10
Camberley
Surrey GU17 7XQ
(High-quality self-compost-
ing toilet system)

The Biolet
Wendage Pollution Control
Rangeways Farm
Conford, Liphook
Hants GU30 7QP
(Ideal for cottages)

Craft supplies
Hobby Horse
15-17 Langton St
London SW10 OJL

Drinks cans
Can Crusher (household)
Available from wholefood
stores or Green Store Mail
Order, Freepost, Bath BA1
2XF

Donald Peters Associates
Elm Cottage
Great Warley St
Warley
Nr Brentwood CM13 3JP
(Can-crushers for all uses)

The Supercan Crusher
(1200 capacity)
Drinks Can Recycling
9 Kingfisher Court
281 Farnham Rd, Slough
Berks SL2 1JF
(With optional sorting
device for separating aluminium and steel)

**Energy-saving
equipment**
Centre for Alternative
Technology Mail-Order
Catalogue - see address
p.278)

Green Light Catalogue
(Lighting)

11B High St
Shepton Mallet
Somerset BA4 5AA
Tel. 0749 346135
(Mail-order service for low-
energy lighting)

Marlec Engineering Co Ltd
Unit K
Cavendish Courtyard
Sallow Rd, Corby
Northants NN7 1DZ
(Wind and solar systems)

SAVAPlug
ECO Marketing Ltd
Queen Anne House
Charlotte St, Bath
Avon BA1 2NE
(The plug includes circuitry
that improves fridge and
freezer motor efficiency)

Thermomax Solar Energy
Systems
Rayotec
London Rd
Sunningdale SL5 ODJ
(All-weather solar water
heaters)

Wind and Sun - Safe Energy
Supplies
The Howe, Watlington
Oxford
Oxon OX9 5EX
Tel. 049161 3859
(Range of renewable energy
equipment ideal for battery
charging and remote energy
requirements)

Yorkpark
16 St George's Industrial
Estate
White Lion Rd
Amersham
Bucks HP7 9JQ
(High-efficiency, low-pollu-
tion gas-condensing boiler)

Furniture

Jarabosky
PO Box 112, Halifax
W.Yorks HX5 0SZ
(Hardwood furniture craft-
ed from obsolete railway
sleepers)

Atelier Furniture
Glenholm
George Street
Nailsworth
Glos. GL6 OAG

Garden equipment

For hiring equipment check
Yellow Pages and garden
centres.

Hamster Baskets
Much Marcle
Ledbury
Herefordshire HR8 2PD
(Clips to reuse spare pieces
of glass as cloches)

Paxton
Pillory St
Nantwich
Cheshire CW5 5BP
(Water butts and plant tubs
made from post-consumer
recycled plastic)

Melcourts
Eight Bells House
Tetbury Glos. GL8 8JG
(Soil conditioners and
mulches from organic bark)

Chase Organics
Coombelands House
Addlestone
KT15 1HY
(Organic gardening equip-
ment plus plants)

Glass

For details of your nearest
bottle bank or glass collection scheme, consult your
local authority or Yellow
Pages.

Midsummer Imports
5-10 Eastman Rd
The Vale
London W3 7YG
(Supplies green and blue
recycled glass)

Junk mail

Mailing Preference Service
(UK)
Freepost 22
London W1E 7EZ
(Get your name removed
from mailing lists by writing
to them)

Nappies/Diapers

Alternatives to disposable
nappies include reusable
cloth nappies, and nappy-
washing services. Contact
the Women's
Environmental Network for
details.

Babykins Products (UK) Ltd
51 Lichfield Rd
Aston
Birmingham B6 5RW

Ecology Kids (non-dispos-
able)
Available from branches of
Mothercare, Toys R US,
John Lewis Partnership
(UK) and mail order (Tel.
0353 668128)

Kooshie Nappies
PHP
12 Thornton Place
London W1H 1FL
(Washable cloth nappies)

Schmidt Natural Clothing
Gamberhead Cottage
Wormelow
Herefordshire HR2 8JJ
(Reusable cotton/wool nap-
pies)

Newspaper

Newspaper Log Maker -
converts newspapers and
other uncoated papers to
solid logs suitable for burning. Contact mail-order
suppliers.

Potmaker - recycle your
newspaper to create plant
pots for seedlings. Kit contains maple wood mould
and instructions. Whole
pot can be planted out.
Available from Henry
Doubleday (see p.279).

Tobil Products
Unit 12F
Hardwick Industrial Estate
Bury St Edmunds
Suffolk IP33 2QH
(Kits for making flower
pots from used newsprint)

Warmcel
Energy Ways
Lordship Cottage
Barwick Rd
Standon
Herts SG11 1PR
(Loft insulation made from
recycled paper)

Paints

Saffron Building & Design
Company
16 Church St
Saffron Walden
Essex CB10 1JW
(Suppliers of German Auro
Organic Paints, plant-based
indoor wall paint, beeswax,
and other cleaning
compounds)

Nutshell Natural Paints
Newtake Cottage,
Taverton
Devon TQ9 6PE
(Paints, wallpaper pastes,
varnishes manufactured

using both modern and traditional techniques and proven natural materials)

Paper (recycled)
Check Yellow Pages for suppliers or contact relevant recycling organizations.

Conservation Papers Ltd
228 London Rd
Reading RG6 1AH

Ecologically Sound Papers
Middleway Workshops
Summertown
Oxford OX2 7LG
(Promotes reclaimed, recycled and alternative papers)

Paper Back
Bow Triangle Business Centre
Unit 2, Eleanor St
London E3 4NP
(Specialist recycled paper merchant)

Universal Office Supplies
Trident Way
International Trading Estate
Brent Rd, Southall
Middlesex
(Range of recycled office products)

Zweckform UK Ltd
Merchant Drive Industrial Estate
Mead Lane, Hertford
Herts SG13 7AY
(100% recycled stationery products)

HCS Infotec
Hoescht House
50 Salisbury Rd, Hounslow
Middlesex
(The first fax paper made from 50% recycled paper content)

Postcards with a message - "You have just won my support/You have just lost my support", with sentences explaining why, for example "Your products are overpackaged", with boxes for the sender to tick. Available from Women's Environmental Movement, UK (see p.279)

Recycling containers
Local authorities usually offer discounted prices, or even free containers, to participants.

Plastoplan UK
Parham Airfield
Parham, Woodbridge
Suffolk IP13 9AF
(Refuse and recycling containers, including bio-bins)

Better Bins Designs Ltd
Victoria Court
Meadowcroft Lane
Ripponden
West Yorks. HX6 4AJ
(Household bins)

Paxton
Pillory St, Nantwich
Cheshire CW5 5BP
(Range includes oil recovery banks, kerbside boxes, office recycling bins, twin bin litter bins)

Taylor & Co Ltd
Hartlebury, Kidderminster
Worcs.
(Containers based on mini-wheeled recycling system)

Scrapstores
Also known as Play Projects - ask at local libraries or contact the Federation of Resource Centres, c/o Playworks,
25 Bullivant St , StAnns,
Nottingham

Vermiculture
Original Organics Ltd
Unit 4-5, Farthings Lodge
Business Centre
Plymtree, Cullompton
Devon EX15 2JY

Water-saving devices
Cisternmiser Ltd
Unit 1
Woodley Park Estate
59-69 Reading Rd
Woodley, Reading
RG5 3AN

Rain Miser
Blackwall Products
Unit 4, Riverside Industrial Estate, River Way
London SE10 0BH
(Device to make the most of rain water, in conjunction with a water butt)

Slurpy - pumping device designed to empty used bathwater into garden watering system. Available from Henry Doubleday.

Soakerhose kit - porous pipe to prevent water wastage, available from garden suppliers.

Toilet dams - from mail-order catalogues or specialist plumbing stores.

Toilet Lid Sink - Allows you to wash hands before water is routed into toilet bowl.

Water butts - recycled 200-litre (45-gallon) drums. Available from Henry Doubleday Association.

Index

Magazines and books

Biocycle - Journal of Waste Recycling/Composting 419 State Avenue Emmaus PA 18049 USA

ENDS Report Finsbury Business Centre 40 Bowling Green Lane London EC1R 0NE

Garbage - The Practical Journal for lthe Environment PO Box 51647 Boulder CO 80321 1647 USA

Green Magazine Hainault Rd Little Heath Romford, Essex RM6 5NP

WARMER Bulletin 83 Mount Ephraim Tunbridge Wells Kent TN4 8BS

Ekins, P, Hillman M, and Hutchison R, *Wealth Beyond Measure: An Atlas of New Economics*, Gaia Books, London, 1992

Friends of the Earth, *Recycling Officer's Handbook*, 1991

Girardet, H, *The Gaia Atlas of Cities: New Directions for Sustainable Urban Living*, Gaia Books, London, 1993

Ogilvie, S M, *A Review of the Environmental Impact of Recycling*, Warren Springs Laboratory, UK, 1992

Woll, N and Feldman, E, *Plastics - America's Packaging Dilemma*, Environmental Action Coalition, Island Press, 1991

Women's Environmental Network, *A Tissue of Lies? - Disposable Paper and the Environment*, London, 1990

Worldwatch Institute, *State of the World - Progress Towards a Sustainable Society*, Earthscan, London

GLOSSARY

Appropriate technology The right tool, used for the right skill, in the right place.

Biodegradable products Materials capable of being broken down into their constituent parts by micro-organisms and bacteria.

CFCs (chlorofluorocarbons) Compounds containing chlorine and fluorine found in home insulation materials, as coolants and insulating materials in fridges and air-conditioning systems.

Co-disposal Disposing of liquid industrial waste and household domestic waste in the same site.

Effluent Unwanted liquid waste from industrial processes and sewage works, often containing toxic heavy metals.

Greenhouse gases Naturally occurring gases, such as carbon dioxide, nitrous oxide, methane, and ozone, and man-made gases like CFCs.

High-grade recycling Where the recycling process creates items of comparable, or only slightly lowered, quality to the original.

Low-grade recycling Where materials are recycled and the end result is a product that is either weaker or lower in quality than the original.

Putrescibles Waste such as food, which decays through anaerobic and aerobic processes

Valorization The value of recycling should be realized in the most appropriate way: incineration with energy recovery for unreclaimable materials.

Author's acknowledgements
By the time this book reaches its final stage of the journey - the book store - a few people involved in its production may be in need of a little restoration and recovery themselves! I would like to thank the team at Gaia for believing me when I said that recycling was a rapidly changing issue and was there any possibility of making yet more changes to the book? To Jo Godfrey Wood, the editor, for her patience, sensitive pruning, and her contributions to the text. To Joss Pearson for her sharp insight and inspiration. And thanks also go to Jonathan Hilton, Katherine Pate, and Janine Christley for their editorial work. And also to Sara Mathews for her design, and Phil Gamble and Tiffany Pearson for their illustrations.

Thanks to everyone who supplied information and to all those whose work and ideas I have drawn on. Particular mentions should go to *Biocycle* magazine, *ENDS* journal, and *Warmer* bulletin. Thanks also to the Earth Works Co-op in Berkeley, California, for their wonderful handbooks. I would also like to acknowledge colleagues Chas Ball, Jeff Cooper, Mike Flood, Andy Moore, former staff and board members of Friends of the Earth, and members of the National Recycling Forum. Some material used in the book was gathered as part of a study, made possible by a research grant from the Leverhulme Trust. My thanks go to them for enabling me to visit the United States and particularly Seattle.

I would like to extend special thanks to John Button for early help and advice; to Jeff Cooper, London Waste Regulation Authority, for reading the completed manuscript and to Jonathon Porritt who, despite his heavy timetable, still managed to contribute the Foreword.

Recycling is a cyclical and ideally an endless process. Writing this book has been a bit like that. As soon as parts were completed, new developments happened. Keeping up to date assumed nightmarish proportions. So finally, to Chris Church, my colleague and partner, I would like to say "Yes, the book is now finished!", and many, many thanks along the way for your love and support.

Publisher's acknowledgements
Gaia Books would like to thank: Phil Gamble for illustrations in *Ideas and Action*, Tiffany Pearson for illustrations in *The Recycler's A to Z*; Matthew Cooper and Richard Jenkins for chapter opener illustrations; Jeremy Hartley/Panos, Lois Walpole, Ilisha Helfman/Elisabeth at the Crafts Council, and Malcolm Fowler and Nancy Fouts at Fouts and Fowler for providing images: Suzy Boston and Eleanor Lines for editorial help: Tradespools Ltd for typesetting: Technographic for reproduction; Dave Whelan, Peter Dubbin, and FMT for scanning;

Also originated by Gaia Books: